Philosophical Problems of Natural Science

Dudley Shapere
UNIVERSITY OF CHICAGO

Sources in Philosophy

A MACMILLAN SERIES
Lewis White Beck, General Editor
THE MACMILLAN COMPANY, NEW YORK
COLLIER–MACMILLAN LIMITED, LONDON

First Printing
Library of Congress catalog card number: 65–11069
THE MACMILLAN COMPANY, NEW YORK
COLLIER-MACMILLAN CANADA, LTD., TORONTO, ONTARIO
Printed in the United States of America

Contents

Introduction

I. PHILOSOPHY OF SCIENCE IN THE TWENTIETH CENTURY

The words "philosophy" and "science" have been linked in such expressions as "scientific philosophy" or "philosophy of science" to describe many different sorts of investigations. To some thinkers, for instance, philosophy and science come together in an attempt to draw out "implications" (or "applications") of scientific fact or method for other fields of human activity, such as ethics, politics, religion, or even all areas of inquiry. Still others, arguing (or assuming) that science requires nonscientific presuppositions in order to guarantee the trustworthiness of its methods or the attainability of its goals, have felt that their task was to discover and examine critically such "foundations" of science.

The main stream of work that has gone by the name "philosophy of science" in the twentieth century, however, has forsaken or at least postponed such tasks, and for compelling reasons. It is not so much that those who have engaged in the sorts of enterprises outlined above have misunderstood the *facts* of science (though they have often erred in that respect too); rather, it is that for the most part they have failed to understand what science is all about—that they have begun with inaccurate or ill-defined conceptions of the nature of science. That is, their discussions have tended to take as point of departure one or another interpretation of what science is and does (for example, that it in some sense "constructs theories" on the basis of "evidence" in order to give "explanations" of "the facts"), and those interpretations, even when supported by arguments, have proved on close examination to be unclear or confused or fallacious or inadequate to the spirit of science. And surely before asserting (for example) that "scientific method" should be applied to political or moral issues, or that science can accomplish its aims only if it makes certain "metaphysical" assumptions which it itself cannot validate, we should try to be as clear as possible as to just what it is we are saying. We should try to be as clear as possible about the meanings of terms we might use, both ordinarily and in philosophical and scientific discourse, in characterizing the aims, methods, and structure of science—terms like "theory," "evidence," "explanation," "fact"; and we should try to be as clear as possible about the ways in which evidence and theory and other elements of science are related to one another.

It is with problems of these kinds—problems of meanings of terms and relationships between elements of science—that philosophers of science in this century have been largely concerned. Naturally, there have been wide differences among them in the ways in which they have approached and dealt with their problems; but nevertheless, they have tended to share certain points of view about what a good treatment should be. The purpose of this anthology is to try to convey an understanding of some of these common attitudes; and it will do so by illustrating the following features of twentieth-century philosophy of science: (1) some of the characteristic ways in which philosophers of science have tended to state their problems—what sorts of formulations they have considered precise enough to permit significant inquiry; (2) the kinds of techniques they have employed in attempting to deal with those problems; and (3) the sorts of answers they have tended to give. Their answers have, of course, frequently met with criticism, which in turn has led to an evolution in viewpoint. Furthermore, in the course of this evolution, even the conceptions of the central problems, and of the techniques for dealing with problems, that have been dominant for most of the past thirty or forty years have themselves been subjected to question, and new conceptions have begun to be developed.

All of these themes will, it is hoped, be visible in the selections to follow. In order to assist the reader in interpreting and relating those selections, this Introduction will provide a background discussion departing from one of the crucial problems of contemporary philosophy of science, the so-called "problem of the meaning of theoretical terms." The evolution, in the face of criticism, of the answers given to this and related questions illustrates clearly the sorts of approaches taken by twentieth-century philosophers of science to the formulation and treatment of their problems.

II. THE PROBLEM OF THEORETICAL TERMS

It must not be supposed that the problems of twentieth-century philosophy of science were wholly unknown to earlier philosophy. For example, the problem of the meaning of theoretical terms, to which we now turn, has its roots in the writings of the great Scottish philosopher, David Hume (1711–76). In the opening pages of his *Treatise of Human Nature*, Hume distinguished between "ideas" and "impressions," declaring (prematurely, as we will see) that "I believe it will not be very necessary to employ many words in explaining this distinction." He divided each of these two classes into "simple" and "complex": "Simple perceptions or impressions and ideas are such as admit of no distinction or separation. The complex are the contrary to these, and may be distinguished into parts. Tho' a particular colour, taste, and smell are qualities all united together in this apple, 'tis easy to perceive they are not the same, but are at least distinguishable from each other." Having made this pair of distinctions, Hume argued that "all our simple ideas in their first appearance are deriv'd from simple impressions, which are correspondent to them, and which they exactly represent." That is, all our ideas must ultimately come from impressions (experience), either directly (as in the case of all simple ideas) or indirectly (as in the case of complex ideas constructed out of simple ones); we can have no idea, however fantastic or imaginative, which is not traceable to an origin in experience. As an argument in support of this contention, Hume noted that "where-ever by any accident the faculties, which give rise to any impressions, are obstructed in their operations, as when one is born blind or deaf; not only the impressions are lost, but also their correspondent ideas; so that there never appear in the mind the least traces of them."

It is now generally agreed that Hume mixed into his argument irrelevant psychological considerations about the origins of our ideas, and that the important core of his discussion is the view that all meaningful terms should be exhaustively definable by a set of elementary terms referring to simple elements of experience, elements which in twentieth-century philosophy have usually been called "sense-data." With this modification, Hume's attempt to ground meaningfulness solidly in experience anticipated some modern answers to a problem that, in the particular form it takes in the philosophy of science, has come to be known as the problem of the meaning of theoretical terms.

This problem arises for philosophers of science in the following way. Certain terms that occur in scientific theories seem to refer to sorts of entities or processes or behavior that are not directly observable. Some classic examples are "force," "field," "atom," "gene," "subconscious," "drive"; usually, terms like "magnetic," "soluble," "elastic," "schizophrenic," and "intelligent" have also been classified as nonobservational, since they seem to refer to "tendencies" or "powers" or "dispositions" of entities rather than to overtly manifested behavior. All such nonobservational terms have been referred to, more positively, as "theoretical" terms. Now, there is a long tradition in philosophy that has looked with suspicion on the entities purportedly referred to by such terms; for science is supposed to be concerned only with what is observable, not with any "metaphysical" entities that may or may not exist behind the scenes of experience, but that cannot in any case be observed. And besides, as Hume pointed out, how could such terms have any meaning beyond what can be said in experiential terms? Hence a large number of philosophers, impressed by such arguments, have maintained that, in spite of appearances, such terms do not really refer to unobservable entities, but are completely definable in experiential terms. Thus anything that is said by means of them can be said equally well without using them at all: they are dispensable and therefore must perform some purely practical function in science, such as conveniently summarizing what, if expressed in purely observational language, might be excessively long-winded and complicated. Bertrand Russell referred to theoretical entities as "logical constructions," and his program for philosophy of science was to show that theoretical terms denote not entities or powers beyond experience at all, but rather concepts built up, by means of the tools of mathematical logic, out of purely experiential elements (sense-data): "Wherever possible," he enjoined us, "logical constructions are to be substituted for inferred entities." [1] Such a view is enormously appealing, since it removes a great deal of the mystery surrounding the relation between "theory" and "fact" in science; for theories are, on this interpretation, mere shorthand summaries of statements that refer solely to actual or possible observations ("possible" as well as "actual" observations, since the events referred to may not be presently occurring—for example, they may be predicted, and the prediction may even be incorrect; such events are therefore unobserved, though nonetheless observ*able*).

These considerations can now be put in the form of a general but precise thesis on which our subsequent discussions can be based. Let us assume that the vocabulary of any scientific theory can be

[1] B. Russell, "The Relation of Sense-Data to Physics," in *Mysticism and Logic* (London: George Allen & Unwin Ltd, 1951), p. 155.

divided into two mutually exclusive classes: (1) one consisting of "observational" terms and (2) the other consisting of all other terms of the theory—these we will call "nonobservational," or "theoretical," terms. (Later, we will have to question the assumption that such a sharp distinction can be made.) The view we have been discussing can then be summarized:

> *Thesis I. Every expression belonging to the theoretical, or nonobservational, vocabulary of a scientific theory is (and must be, if it is not to be meaningless) replaceable without gain or loss of meaning by a set of terms belonging solely to the observational vocabulary.*

Notice that, in our formulation of Thesis I, nothing has been said about the character of the terms occurring in the observational vocabulary. For many of the early twentieth-century followers of Hume, those terms would have to be terms referring to sense-data. But because there are grave difficulties in the notion of a sense-datum vocabulary, the thesis is more conveniently phrased in this general way in order to accommodate alternative views of the sorts of terms to be classed as "observational." For, among other things, it has proved extremely difficult to specify exactly how to tell what terms are to count as sense-datum terms, or to give any clear-cut examples of such terms; and therefore the sense-datum view has found very few adherents in the past twenty or thirty years. More popular have been other views about the nature of an observational vocabulary; and by selecting one of these for detailed consideration, we will be able to bring out some objections that have been raised generally against any form of Thesis I.

III. OPERATIONALISM AS A VERSION OF THESIS I

The view that we will discuss is Operationalism (or Operationism), first advanced by P. W. Bridgman in *The Logic of Modern Physics* (1927). "What," Bridgman asks, "do we mean by the length of an object? We evidently know what we mean by the length if we can tell what the length of any and every object is, and for the physicist nothing more is required. To find the length of an object, we have to perform certain physical operations. The concept of length is therefore fixed when the operations by which length is measured are fixed: that is, the concept of length involves as much as and nothing more than the set of operations by which length is determined. In general, we mean by any concept nothing more than a set of operations; *the concept is synonymous with the corresponding set of operations.* If the concept is physical, as of length, the operations are actual physical operations . . . or if the concept is mental, as of mathematical continuity, the operations are mental operations, namely those by which we determine whether a given aggregate of magnitude is continuous." [2] Thus Bridgman's version of Thesis I is that *every meaningful scientific term must be either definable exhaustively in terms of a specific and unambiguous set of possible operations, or be itself a term denoting such an operation.*

There are serious difficulties with this view. First, what is meant by an "operation"? We think first of manipulations of instruments; but as the passage quoted from Bridgman indicates, this is not enough to account for the meaningfulness of all scientific concepts: operationalists were forced to admit varieties of noninstrumental operations also. But as Hempel has pointed out with regard to such noninstrumental operations, "In operationist writings, these symbolic procedures have been characterized so vaguely as to permit the introduction, by a suitable choice of 'verbal' or 'mental' operations, of virtually all those ideas that operational analysis was to prohibit as devoid of meaning." [3]

Second, even if we can make clear the notion of an operation, what is meant by a "possible" operation as opposed to an "impossible" one? Three interpretations suggest themselves. (1) A suggested operation may be *technically possible*, in the sense that it is possible under current theory, but no way is known of actually carrying out the operation. But clearly this will not do justice to what the operationalist has in mind: we would not want to say that the expression "photographing the moon's other side" was meaningless until the technical problem of shooting a camera-carrying satellite around the moon was solved. (2) The relevant sense may then be that of *theoretical* possibility or impossibility: an operation is possible or impossible depending on whether it is allowable in terms of current scientific theory (independently of the "purely technical problem" of whether we can carry it out). Thus it is not technically

[2] P. W. Bridgman, *The Logic of Modern Physics* (New York: The Macmillan Co., 1946), p. 5.

[3] C. G. Hempel, "A Logical Appraisal of Operationism," in P. Frank (ed.), *The Validation of Scientific Theories* (Boston: The Beacon Press, 1956), p. 57.

possible (as yet) to travel to distant stars; still, in terms of the laws of physics as currently known, such a possibility is not excluded; interstellar travel is "theoretically possible." But if this sense of "possible" were taken as the one relevant to the operationalist view, a severe restriction would be placed on the ability of science to progress according to operationalist criteria; for speculation in terms of "operations" not countenanced by current theory would be outlawed not merely as false, but as gibberish. And certainly much of scientific progress has consisted of the introduction of new concepts that did not make sense according to previous theories. It will not do to try to escape this objection by appealing to the laws of nature (whether known or not) rather than to the laws known to current science in order to specify what is and what is not possible; for since we can never know whether our current laws are the true laws of nature, we can never know, with regard to a proposed operation that has not been performed, whether it is possible in this sense, and so whether we are talking utter nonsense. (3) It will not do, either, to interpret "possible" in terms of "what is not logically self-contradictory"; for the result will then be overly broad. A statement like, "The earth is at rest in absolute space," containing the expression "absolute space," which operationalism hoped to banish, is perfectly consistent logically. And the term "absolute space" itself, while it may suffer from other defects, does not, at least, appear to be self-contradictory. Clearly what is needed for operationalism is some sense of "possible" intermediate between "possible in terms of currently known laws" (which excludes too much) and "possible" in the sense of "logically noncontradictory" (which lets in too much). The problem is how to specify this intermediate sense clearly and precisely.[4]

What we are most interested in at present, however, is the question of whether scientific concepts can in general be *exhaustively* defined in operational terms; and so we may, for the sake of argument, suppose that objections such as the above, which have to do with the difficulty of simply understanding what operationalism is asserting, can be overcome. The question of whether all scientific concepts can be defined exhaustively in operational terms is, of

---

[4] Similar difficulties arise with regard to the "Verifiability Theory of Meaning," according to which the meaning of a *statement* (rather than of a term, as in operationalism) is to be specified in terms of a set of *possible* methods of verification.

course, only a special case of the general problem concerning Thesis I, namely, whether all theoretical terms of a scientific theory can be defined exhaustively in terms of an observational vocabulary, however conceived. The issues revolving around this problem are discussed in the first selection of this anthology, Carl Hempel's "The Theoretician's Dilemma." Hempel presents and evaluates many of the major arguments for and against the Thesis in a way which, as he says, is "independent of precisely where the dividing line between the terms of the observational and theoretical vocabularies is drawn."

IV. LOGIC AS A MODEL AND TOOL FOR PHILOSOPHY OF SCIENCE

Before examining some of the views and problems discussed by Hempel, let us notice some general aspects of the way he and those he discusses approach their problems—their conceptions of their tasks and of the techniques to be used to perform them. It is characteristic of their work, and indeed of perhaps most of the work done in philosophy of science in this century, that it makes extensive use of the modern techniques of mathematical logic: the problems are formulated, wherever possible, in terms of that logic, and one criterion of success of an analysis is the extent to which it is performed in terms of that logic. Rudolf Carnap, in whose works many of the contemporary discussions of the problem of theoretical terms (as well as many other problems of the philosophy of science) originate, spoke of his subject as being "the logic of science," and he even claimed that all philosophy is (or should be replaced by) the logic of science. In order to understand the idea behind this expression, it will be necessary to examine the distinction often drawn in elementary logic texts between the "content" of a proposition or argument and its "form," logic being concerned only with the latter. Thus logic is not interested in the truth or falsity of the statements, "All Greeks are men," or "All men are mortal," or even in the fact that these specific statements imply the conclusion, "All Greeks are mortal." Rather, logic is concerned with the general *form* of proposition ("All S is P") and of argument ("All S is P, all P is Q; therefore all S is Q") of which such specific statements and arguments are mere instances. Modern logic deals with these and far more complicated forms of statements and arguments in symbolic terms, and studies their general characteristics (it also studies the concepts used in talking about such statements and arguments, for example, "truth" and "proof").

Similarly, "the logic of science" is conceived of as a subject concerned, not with the truth or falsity of the particular propositions of science (the "content" of science)—that is the job of the scientist—but with the general types or forms of expressions with which science deals, with the general rules according to which conclusions are correctly arrived at in science, and with the concepts used in discussing scientific expressions and arguments (for example, "meaningful," "explanation," "law"). As to the sorts of terms that supply the "content" to this "form," it is interested in them only insofar as it studies general rules governing what kind of content can be utilized (for example, that the terms filling the content-places of the logical forms of scientific propositions must denote "operations" or be "operationally definable"). It follows that philosophy of science, so conceived, is immune to the vicissitudes of science—the coming and going of particular theories; for those changes have to do with the content of science, whereas the philosopher is concerned with its structure—not with specific theories, but with the meaning of "theory" itself.

But not only is "the logic of science" modeled as a subject on the analogy of modern mathematical logic; it also utilizes the powerful techniques of that logic in dealing with its problems. Such use of logic is well illustrated in Rudolf Carnap's arguments, discussed by Hempel, that scientific concepts cannot in general be exhaustively defined and therefore replaced by a set of observational statements (for example, operational definitions). In order to understand those arguments, therefore, we will have to gain an understanding of some of the simpler relevant logical notions and techniques.

Logicians use the letters "p" and "q" (and others if needed) to stand for propositions or sentences that are true or false, instead of writing them out in full. This permits a saving of space and, by thus subduing the "content" of the propositions, calls attention to the form or structure of an argument. These letters, in turn, are joined to one another by various other symbols, called "connectives," to build up more complex propositions. For our purposes, the most important logical connective is "$\supset$." The logician *defines* this symbol so that the proposition "$p \supset q$" is false whenever "p" is true and "q" false (no matter what sentences "p" and "q" may stand for). In this respect, "$p \supset q$" corresponds to the expression "if-then," which functions in ordinary English as a connective: for a sentence like, "If John succeeds, then Mary is happy," is false if "John succeeds" is true but "Mary is happy" is false. Hence, on the basis of this correspondence, "$p \supset q$" may be read, "If p, then q." In all other cases ("p" true, "q" true; "p" false, "q" true; "p" false, "q" false), the proposition "$p \supset q$" is defined to be true.

Notice that the truth or falsity of the proposition "$p \supset q$" is completely determined no matter *which* of the possibilities with regard to "p" and "q" happens to be realized in nature. This characteristic is shared by all the connectives used in modern mathematical logic: when they join two propositions to form a more complex one, the truth or falsity of the resulting compound is determined in all possible cases by the truth or falsity of the component parts. (Such connectives are called "truth-functional"; sometimes the word "extensional" is also used to refer to this characteristic.) In this sense, just as logic is independent of the meanings of the sentences for which "p" and "q" stand, so also it is independent of what actually is the case; finding out about the latter is the job of observation, and in particular of science.

On the other hand, this "truth-functional" characteristic is not shared by all the connectives used in ordinary English; the notion of causal connection, expressed by the words "causes" or "because," is an example. Even if we know the truth of "Jones died" and "Jones had cancer," the truth of "Jones died because he had cancer" remains undetermined (he may have been shot). Now, very often the expression "if-then" is used in ordinary discourse to express a causal relationship. What this means is simply that "if-then" *as the logician uses it*—the connective "$\supset$"—does not express causal connection. It is by opting for connectives that do have the truth-functional property that logicians are able to concentrate on those facets of arguments whose correctness depends wholly on the form or structure, and not on the content of the propositions concerned.

The logician's interpretation of "if-then," however, has some consequences that are peculiar from the viewpoint of ordinary language: since it is false that Chicago is in Ohio, and true that two plus two equals four, the logical definition of "$\supset$," interpreted as "if-then," makes the statement "If Chicago is in Ohio, then two plus two equals four" true. Similarly, "If Chicago is in Illinois, then two plus two equals four" and "If Chicago is in Ohio, then two plus two equals six" are true. Such consequences may make the logician's use of "if-then" seem arbitrary and perverse and inadequate as an analysis of the ordinary (and scientific) use of "if-then"; and indeed, we will see that many of the troubles of modern philosophy of science have been blamed by some critics on the use of this interpretation of "if-then." But it must be remembered that this interpretation has helped logicians achieve very remarkable results: the notion of "implication" associated with "⊃" (as when we say that "p implies q" in the sense that if "p" is true, then "q" must also be true) has helped connect logic intimately with mathematics, and has helped lead to important discoveries in both fields; and although there may be some sorts of arguments ordinarily considered valid which are not covered by this notion of implication, the large variety of arguments covered are dealt with in a completely satisfactory way. And there remains the possibility that arguments that have not yet been dealt with satisfactorily in terms of this notion will ultimately be brought under its jurisdiction. On the other hand, no one has presented an alternative interpretation (for example, in terms of "causal connections") that has been accepted by many as even being clear.

One last connective will be needed for the discussions to follow: "$p \equiv q$," which may be interpreted as "p if and only if q" (or "if p then q, and if q then p," understanding "if p then q" in the sense defined above). "$p \equiv q$" will be seen to be true in case both "p" and "q" are true, or in case both are false; in the remaining two cases the proposition is false.

V. CRITIQUE OF THESIS I; PARTIAL INTERPRETATION AND THESIS II

We can now return to Carnap's criticism of Thesis I—his reasons for asserting that it is impossible to define theoretical terms exhaustively by means of strictly observational expressions. Consider operational definitions. Conceived of as rules for the replacement of theoretical terms by observational ones, we might suppose them to follow this pattern: an individual x will be said to have a property Q (where "Q" is a theoretical term) if and only if the statement, "If operation C is performed on x, then x will show effects E" is true. The statement, "x has the (theoretical) property Q" is then replaceable without gain or loss of meaning by the "if-then" "operational" statement. For example, this object will be said to be magnetic if and only if the following condition is satisfied: if a small piece of iron is placed near this object, then the piece of iron will move toward the object. If we interpret the "if-then" and the "if and only if" here in the manner of logic, the "operational definition" can be symbolized, "$Qx \equiv (Cx \supset Ex)$." [5]

Unfortunately, as Carnap pointed out, if we take the "if-then" in the logician's sense as in this formula, we get a disastrous result. For if operation C is *not* performed on x (so that "Cx" is false), the whole of "$Cx \supset Ex$" is true, as we saw in the preceding section. And because "$Qx \equiv (Cx \supset Ex)$" is true by definition, we are therefore forced to say that x has the property Q—and any determinate degree thereof—at all times when the operation C is not being performed on it! But while we might be willing to say that an object has weight even when it is not being weighed, we would not want to say that, at all times when it is not being weighed, it has a weight *both* of ten pounds *and* of fifty pounds. Yet this is exactly what we would be forced to say on the above interpretation: if "Cx" is false, then "$Cx \supset Ex$" is true *no matter what* we put for "Ex"; and if "$Cx \supset Ex$" and "$Qx \equiv (Cx \supset Ex)$" are true, then (by the definition of "$\equiv$") "Qx" must be true. Similarly, we would have to say that an object is magnetic at all times when it is not being tested for magnetism; and in this case (unlike that of weight), we would not want to say that all objects not being tested for magnetism are magnetic; and even for objects that we would want to say are magnetic at some times when they are not being subjected to such tests, we would also want to say that they might not be magnetic. But this is exactly what we would be prevented from saying by the above interpretation: for if "Cx" is false (if the tests for magnetism are not being applied), then we *must* say that "Qx" is true (that x is magnetic).

Two possible sources of the difficulty have been suggested: either the logician's interpretation of "if-then" is not the sense that is appropriate to the operational statement (or, more generally, to the

[5] Here we see one of the advantages of symbolization: if this formula were written out in ordinary words, it would have the rather unwieldy form, "x has the property Q if and only if, if x is subjected to test conditions C, it manifests the response E."

As is typical in discussions of this topic, the example given concerns a *property* (the dispositional property magnetism) rather than an *entity* (for example, electromagnetic field or subconscious). The question of theoretical terms purporting to refer to entities is less fundamental than that of such terms ascribing properties to entities if we suppose (as seems usually to be done) that we can treat entities as collections of properties (specifically, of dispositional properties).

observational statement on the right of the "≡" sign); or that use of "if-then" is relevant, but our conception of the relation between theoretical and observational terms as one of mutual replaceability (that is, as "$Qx \equiv (Cx \supset Ex)$") is at fault. The first proposal, as we have indicated, has not led to any widely accepted solution: no interpretation of the relevant sense of "if-then" in terms of "necessary connection," "physical connection," "real connection," and so forth, has as yet been very widely believed even to be promising.

Carnap chose the second alternative; and his choice is a typical illustration of the approach mentioned earlier (Sec. IV), according to which, in the face of difficulties, so many contemporary philosophers of science will try to reformulate their arguments and results before they abandon the sure ground of logic. Carnap proposed, therefore, that theoretical and observational terms are related, not by explicit definitions of the former in terms of the latter, but rather by "reduction sentences" which give only a *partial interpretation* of the theoretical term. The simplest type of reduction sentence is the following: "$Cx \supset (Qx \equiv Ex)$"—that is, "If test conditions C are applied to x, then x has the property Q if and only if x manifests the response E." Here, if test conditions C are not being applied, x does not necessarily have Q, and the earlier difficulties disappear. Q is given only a "partial interpretation" in the sense that this new formulation specifies the meaning of "Q" only for those objects that meet the test conditions C; the meaning of "Q" is left open, in the sense that further reduction sentences, giving further conditions and responses for testing the presence of Q, can always be added.[6]

---

[6] Lack of an operational definition of a term, and even presumed impossibility of giving one, does not in fact always deter scientists from accepting the concept if it accomplishes some important function in the theory. The most famous incident of this type was the acceptance into physics of the notion of the elementary particle called the "neutrino," in spite of the fact that scientists at the time widely supposed that the peculiar conjunction of properties attributed to that entity made it impossible ever to observe. But unless the entity were assumed to exist, physicists would have had to abandon the principle of the conservation of energy; but to abandon that principle, which has such widespread and fundamental application throughout physics, would have been to upset most of that science. On this ground (in spite of the presumed impossibility of observing it or any other effects of it than the one it was introduced to account for—and this is to say that its introduction was an *ad hoc* maneuver), an unobservable particle, the neutrino, was postulated to account for the observed energy imbalance in certain radioactive processes. (The fact that the neutrino was later detected does not detract from the fact that, at the time of its introduction, the

The preceding argument against Thesis I has, then, led to an abandonment of that thesis and its replacement by a new view of the relationship between theoretical and observational terms. The distinction between those two kinds of terms is retained (though the arguments are carefully phrased so as to avoid the difficulties of actually making such a distinction); but now the relationship is conceived of as follows:

> *Thesis II. At least some expressions occurring in a scientific theory can be only partially interpreted in terms of the observational vocabulary.*

Thus the terms of the theoretical vocabulary are not dispensable, even in principle; there are in the concepts of a scientific theory elements of meaning that go beyond what is given in experience. However, according to the proponents of this position, this does not mean a return to the view that the human mind has special insight into a reality beyond experience; for (it is claimed) all the non-experiential meaning of a concept can be accounted for in terms of the place of that concept in a logical system (*cf.*, below, Sec. VII).

The question of whether Carnap is right and Thesis I wrong, however, is complicated by a theorem of mathematical logic proved by William Craig. According to this theorem, if the language of a scientific theory (except for such "purely logical" terms as " $\supset$ " and " $\equiv$ "—*cf.*, below, Sec. VII) is divided into two mutually exclusive classes (observational and theoretical terms), it is always possible to replace that language by another in which none of the terms of the theoretical vocabulary occur. It would seem, therefore, that Thesis I is defensible after all (though in a modified form, since now the language as a whole, rather than particular expressions in it, is replaced). But, as is brought out in the selection by Hempel ("The Theoretician's Dilemma," Sec. 9), Craig's Theorem does not really make Thesis I any more palatable. For in general, the new language replacing the one containing theoretical terms will have the unhelp-

---

particle was thought by many who accepted it to be impossible to observe. Indeed, this case illustrates the difficulty of determining, at any given time in the history of physics, what is "observable" and what is not.) Thus the demand of extreme operationalism that *every* scientific concept be definable operationally does not stand up either. Carnap, as will be seen below, would agree with this point: not all the terms of a scientific theory are even partially interpreted; some are only connected in a logical system with other terms, some of which are partially interpreted.

ful feature (among others) of containing an infinite number of axioms, and so fails to provide the desired clarification of the original system.

VI. THEORETICAL *VS.* OBSERVATIONAL TERMS: THESIS III

One of the chief motivations behind the attempt to defend a distinction between theoretical and observational terms has been the desire to explain how a theory can be tested against the data of experience, and how one theory can be said to "account for the facts" better than another; that is, to give a precise characterization of the idea, almost universally accepted in modern times,[7] that the sciences are "based on experience," that they are "empirical." Thus the adherents of both Theses I and II have reasoned as follows: test of a scientific theory can be accomplished if and only if there are at least some terms, or at least some distinguishable components of the meanings of some terms occurring in the theory, that, by referring to theory-independent elements of experience, have a meaning independent of their theoretical context; and comparison of different scientific theories can be accomplished if and only if there are at least some such terms (or components) that have the *same* meaning in both of those different theories. If there is no such common meaning, the theories are not talking about the same things, and hence cannot be compared with respect to their adequacy. From this viewpoint, even if the distinction between "theoretical" and "observational" terms is not a sharp one, nevertheless there must be

---

[7] *Almost* universally accepted: the view is not unknown in modern philosophy that, if we apply our "reason" carefully enough, we will, independently of any appeal whatsoever to experience, be able to discover certain fundamental truths about the universe from which other truths (including perhaps all of science) can be deduced. In this century, varying the theme slightly, E. A. Milne and Sir Arthur Eddington have maintained that the empirical method itself implies the laws of science—that, if we analyze that method carefully enough, it will become dispensable as a route to obtaining scientific conclusions. Milne, for example, asserts that "as soon as we have carefully stated exactly how we become aware of the quantitative aspects of a phenomenon, then automatically we must be able, given the skill, to infer all the relations that exist between those quantitative aspects." [E. A. Milne, "The Fundamental Concepts of Natural Philosophy," *Proceedings of the Royal Society of Edinburgh,* LXII (1943–44), Part I; reprinted in M. Munitz (ed.), *Theories of the Universe* (Glencoe: The Free Press, 1957), pp. 358–359.]

some overlap of meaning between different theories if they are to be comparable.

Many thinkers, even among those who accept Thesis II, have come to doubt that the distinction is as sharp as many philosophers of the twenties and thirties supposed. After all, under what circumstances exactly are we "merely observing," and not "interpreting" in the light of "theory"? At one extreme, whenever we make judgments of distances on the basis of relative apparent sizes, are we ("unconsciously," perhaps) assuming a knowledge of the geometry of space? Are we merely "observing" when we look through a microscope, even though the microscope has "built into it" a great deal of theoretical knowledge of optics? (Are such observations, then—and all observations—really "loaded" to at least some degree with theory?) And at the other extreme—of terms typically classed as "theoretical" —do scientists not, after all, "observe" atoms and protons and even neutrinos? (Or do they only observe their effects? But even if we can never observe them, but only their effects, is this sufficient ground for classifying them as "theoretical"? For some philosophers have argued that we never observe *any* material objects, but can only observe their effects on our senses or our minds.) And even if we do ordinarily make a distinction between observational and theoretical language, is it relevant to the analysis of science in the profound way attributed to it by the adherents of Theses I and II? For, as Pierre Duhem points out, the scientist will not, in reply to a question, say (for example) that he is "studying the oscillations of the piece of iron carrying this mirror"; rather, he will say that he is "measuring the electrical resistance of a coil." That is, even when they are reporting their "observations," scientists do not use what would in any ordinary sense be referred to as an "observation" language in a pure sense. Rather, they use language that already presupposes a great deal of understanding of scientific theory.

In the light of such considerations as these, some recent philosophers have claimed that the distinction between observational and theoretical terms is a matter of degree rather than of kind, so that a sharp line between them will be at worst arbitrary, at best merely convenient, the position of the line varying from person to person and from context to context; in particular, the scientist's report of observations will be relatively heavily laden with theory. Hence the advocates of Thesis II, realizing that the distinction may not be an absolute one, have in recent years tried to put their arguments in ways that would be independent of just how that distinction is to be made (*cf.*, Hempel's remarks at the end of Sec. 2 of "The Theoretician's Dilemma").

Other thinkers, however, have gone still further, arguing that all the terms in a scientific theory are "theory-laden" or "theory-dependent" in the following radical sense:

> *Thesis III. It is impossible (at least in most cases) to segregate a component of the meanings of terms occurring in different theories such that those theories will have the same, or overlapping, observational vocabularies; even though the same terms may occur in those different theories, those terms do not have the same meanings, for meaning depends intimately on, and varies with, theoretical context.*

A view that at least approaches this extreme position is presented in the selection by Stephen Toulmin. He emphasizes that the sorts of "phenomena" that set problems for the scientist are those that deviate from an expected pattern or normality; such presuppositions as to what needs to be explained he calls "ideals of natural order" or "paradigms." But not only do these "ideals" *select* which experiences are problematical; Toulmin holds that the "phenomena" are even *defined* by those ideals. He tells us (in a passage not contained in our selection) of "the continual interaction of theory with fact—the way in which theories are built on facts, while at the same time giving significance to them and even determining what are 'facts' for us at all." [8] And he argues that "Men who accept different ideals and paradigms . . . will not even *have* the same problems; events which are 'phenomena' in one man's eyes will be passed over by the other as 'perfectly natural.'"

Still more radical is the view presented by Thomas Kuhn in his *The Structure of Scientific Revolutions.* In his view, the "paradigms" that constitute the ways in which scientists of different traditions view the world, and that guide them when they frame their experiments and theories, are "incommensurable." A paradigm determines what the scientist of a given tradition takes to be the facts, what his problems are, and the standards he requires a theory to meet; and all these will, in general, vary from paradigm to paradigm. For example, since (according to Kuhn) Newtonian physics is based on a paradigm different from Einstein's, the latter is not, as it is usually

[8] S. Toulmin, *Foresight and Understanding* (Bloomington: Indiana Univ. Press, 1961), p. 95.

taken to be, a more general and accurate version of the former; terms such as "space," "time," "mass," and the like, have entirely different meanings in the two theories.

Yet if the meanings of all terms are theory- (or paradigm-) determined to the extent that the meanings even of the same terms in different theoretical contexts cannot be compared, and have absolutely nothing in common, we must wonder, with those who have tried to defend a distinction between theoretical and observational terms, how those theories are to be judged against one another, and how the replacement of one theory by another can be said to constitute "progress," an "advance." Kuhn is aware of this difficulty: in some passages which are not included in our selection, he claims that after a scientific revolution, in which one paradigm replaces another, "the whole network of fact and theory . . . has shifted." [9] Hence, "Practicing in different worlds, the two groups of scientists see different things when they look from the same point in the same direction." [10] Nevertheless, he declares, "that is not to say that they can see anything they please. Both are looking at the world, and what they look at has not changed." [11] But it is difficult to see how this qualification (and the distinction hinted at between "seeing" and "looking at") is at all consistent with his view that scientific vocabularies are "incommensurable," or how in any case it would dispel the extreme relativism implied in his view that "The competition between paradigms is not the sort of battle that can be resolved by proofs." [12] Kuhn's qualifications seem more the statement of the problem he and those who hold similar views must face—of how two "incommensurable" theories can be compared—than a solution of that problem. Indeed, Kuhn's view seems to imply that a theory is not accepted because it is better than any alternatives; on the contrary, it is called "better" because it is accepted.

Toulmin does try to provide an answer to the difficulty: "How do we know which presuppositions to adopt? Certainly, explanatory paradigms and ideals of natural order are not 'true' or 'false' in any naive sense. Rather, they 'take us further (or less far),' and are theoretically more or less 'fruitful.'" But "fruitful" in accomplishing

[9] T. S. Kuhn, *The Structure of Scientific Revolutions* (Chicago: Univ. of Chicago Press, 1963), p. 140.

[10] *Ibid.*, p. 149.

[11] *Ibid.*, p. 149.

[12] *Ibid.*, p. 147.

what? Toward what goals does one theory "take us further" than another? Certainly one ideal, one set of presuppositions, is not better than another in the sense that it enables us to deal more effectively with the same problems, or with the same facts; for these, on Toulmin's view, differ from ideal to ideal. Like Kuhn, Toulmin offers us little in the way of clarification of the sense in which one theory can be judged more acceptable than another.

We are thus left with a dilemma: either we accept the distinction between theoretical and observational terms (in some form or other), or we reject it. If we accept it, then, although we will have gained the advantage of making scientific theories subject to the tribunal of facts that are independent of them, we will be left with the task of making this distinction precise, or at least of showing how elements that allow comparison of different theories are distinguishable. If we reject it, then although we will evade its undeniable difficulties, we will be confronted with the problem of explaining how two different theories can be compared and judged. Both of these alternatives must overcome formidable difficulties, some of which have been outlined here. One of the outstanding problems of the philosophy of science today is to steer a safe course between the horns of this dilemma.

VII. THEORIES AND AXIOMATIC SYSTEMS

In examining the problem of theoretical terms, we have seen how, in the face of critical analysis, there has been an evolution of views. But there is more behind the shift from Thesis II to Thesis III than a mere change with regard to the answer to a single problem; for underlying the viewpoint of Thesis III is a fundamental change in what may be called "philosophical style"—in the ways of formulating and dealing with problems. For the adherents of that view, mathematical logic is no longer the key to the solution of philosophical problems of science. We will be able to appreciate this change of viewpoint more fully, however, if we first survey some other topics which are central in recent controversies (and in the selections to follow).

One of these topics concerns the extent to which logic can be used to reveal the nature of a scientific theory. Basic to the discussion in Hempel's "The Theoretician's Dilemma," as well as to a great number of writings of those who have held that mathematical logic is a tool for understanding science, is a view of a scientific theory as an *interpreted axiomatic system*. The notion of an axiomatic system is intuitively obvious, especially to anyone who has studied elementary geometry: a set of statements (usually divided into definitions, axioms, and postulates, though for our purposes this is irrelevant) is accepted at the outset, and further statements (theorems) are proved on the basis of them. This intuitive notion, however, has undergone the most rigorous development at the hands of modern logicians, and a very precise analysis has been made of the character of the terms that occur in the axioms, the ways in which those terms are put together into the statements formulating the axioms, and the notion of deduction or proof by which we arrive at theorems.

To appreciate this work and its application to the philosophy of science, we must first understand what the logician means by an *un*interpreted axiomatic system. Like anything else, such a system must be formulated in terms of a language; and even the notion of a language has been given a precise treatment by logicians, through their notion of a *formal language*. Let us approach this notion via an analogy. Ordinary dictionaries define words circularly—that is, if we look up a word, and then look up all the words used to define it, and so on, we will soon find words being defined in terms of the very words we looked up earlier. Suppose someone were to try to remove this circularity by listing relatively few simple words (which he calls "basic," or *"primitive," "terms"*) whose meanings are taken to be clear, and which are adequate to define all the remaining words in the dictionary (which he calls "defined terms"). The defined terms are thus dispensable, in principle at least, since whatever could be said by using them could be said without them, by using only primitive terms. Now suppose he were to go further, writing a book in which he lists the rules according to which his basic terms may be combined to form meaningful phrases and sentences; these he calls "grammatical rules," or *"rules of formation"* of phrases and sentences. Thus, if *apple, grow, on,* and *tree* are taken as primitive terms of his dictionary, then he tries to formulate rules such that "Apples grow on trees" will be a grammatically "well-formed" sentence, while "On grow trees apples" is not. One trouble he would face is that, in languages such as English, the job of formulating such rules is extremely complicated: so many variations are possible, and any rules have a multitude of exceptions. For this reason—as well as to gain insight into questions like that of the nature of a system or theory—the logician deals with artificial languages which have the features brought out in this analogy, but without their complexity.

A *formal language*, then, consists of a precise listing of *primitive terms*, plus a set of restrictions, in the form of precise *rules of formation*, according to which these primitive terms can be combined with one another into *well-formed formulas*. The primitive terms consist of purely logical terms (like the connectives "⊃" and "≡," or perhaps others in terms of which these can be defined) and also of "nonlogical" ones (which we may consider to be the "theoretical" and "observational" terms of the language—unless, of course, all the theoretical terms are defined terms). In addition to the primitive terms, there will generally also be defined terms, but they are in principle dispensable.

This, then, is the formal language. Against this background of primitive terms and rules of formation, an *axiomatic system* is now constructed: a set of well-formed formulas is selected; these will be the *axioms* of the system. Precisely specified *rules of transformation* (or *inference* or *deduction*) then determine a class of *theorems* which can be deduced from those axioms. (In terms of our earlier analogy, suppose our scholar, having laid down the rules for forming grammatically meaningful sentences, now selects a few sentences which he takes to be true, and then, in accordance with the rules of logic, tries to deduce from them other true statements—perhaps he will hope to select his axioms so wisely that *all* other true statements in his language will be so deducible.)

A highly important feature of our discussion is that, up to this point, no understanding of the primitive terms is presupposed: as far as the logician is concerned, they are *uninterpreted* in the sense that he need consider them to have no meaning apart from the restrictions on the ways in which they can be combined with one another according to the rules of formation. Even the nonlogical terms can be treated as being mere dummy symbols which enter according to certain rules into logical formulas. All this is, of course, just another aspect of the fact that logicians are concerned with the "form" rather than with the "content" of propositions and deductions.

Therefore, if we are to consider a scientific theory to be an axiomatic system, we have thus far only the skeleton, so to speak, of such a theory: we need to *interpret* the primitive terms. For the adherents of Theses I and II, the question is this (we pass over the problem of interpreting purely logical primitives): How do we interpret those primitives that are "observational" and "theoretical" terms (supposing there to be such a distinction, and supposing both types to be among the primitives)? Hempel's view of such interpretation is that we take "observational" primitives as "antecedently understood"; but because he finds a problem in trying to understand theoretical terms, they cannot be so taken—they will have to be interpreted via the observational ones. To accomplish this, according to Hempel, we introduce what he calls "interpretative statements," or "rules," which "connect certain terms of the theoretical vocabulary with observational terms." In this way, we get an interpreted axiomatic system; and a scientific theory is understood to be such a system.[13]

From this point of view, the question of the relation between theoretical and observational terms reduces to the question of the extent to which theoretical terms can be connected via such interpretative rules with observational ones. Carnap's view, for example, is that (1) some theoretical terms are connected with the observational vocabulary only by partial interpretations in terms of reduction sentences; (2) other theoretical terms are connected only with other theoretical terms, through the rules of formation of the system. There are also conceptions of interpretative statements other than reduction sentences and operational definitions (in the old sense); some (for example, "Campbellian dictionary") are discussed by Hempel in Sec. 8 of "The Theoretician's Dilemma." In that section, he tries to provide a general analysis applicable to any type of interpretative statement whatever, in terms of the notion of an "interpretative system."

The conception of a scientific theory as an interpreted axiomatic system has, however, been criticized as being too narrow, and even as distorting the true character of scientific theories. Such criticisms will be discussed shortly.

---

[13] As Hempel suggests, a new "interpreted theory" (or "system") can be constructed whose axioms consist of the axioms of the uninterpreted system plus the interpretative rules.

It should be noted that the mathematical formulas of a scientific theory (insofar as they are uninterpreted) are generally agreed to be formulable in logical terms (provided "logic" is understood in a fairly broad sense).

VIII. LAWLIKENESS AND COUNTERFACTUAL CONDITIONALS

The notion of "scientific law," like the notion of "scientific theory," provides another basis for controversy among the authors of our selections. We will here outline one of the chief problems facing any attempt to deal with that notion by utilizing the techniques of modern logic.

According to a view that takes Hume's analysis of causality as its point of departure, laws are nothing but generalizations based on the invariable connection between certain past experiences; besides "universality," there is, on the Humean view, no further element, such as "necessity," asserted by any statement of scientific law. The major objection repeatedly urged against this view is that it fails to distinguish between accidental generalizations and lawlike statements. (The expression "lawlike statement" covers not only laws, but also statements thought to be laws, but which are not because they are false.) That is, it is asserted, the Humean analysis fails to note any difference between such statements as, "All the sugar in this room is soluble in water" (a lawlike statement) and "All the people in this room are wearing green socks" (an accidental generalization or coincidence). Hume's view, according to those who raise this objection, will be overthrown if this distinction can be made successfully.

How, then, is the distinction to be maintained? In other words, inasmuch as both lawlike statements and mere accidental generalizations are of the form, "All S is P" (or some more complicated form of universal statement), what additional characteristics distinguish lawlike from nonlawlike universal statements? One proposal is as follows: that lawlike statements provide support for "counterfactual conditionals," whereas accidental generalizations do not. (A counterfactual conditional is a statement of the form, "If (contrary to what is the case) S were the case, then P would be the case." Note that the statement is in the subjunctive mood.) For example, the statement, "All sugar placed in water dissolves," supports the statement, "If this sugar (which is not in water) were placed in water, it would dissolve." On the other hand, the statement, "All the people in this room are wearing green socks," does not support the corresponding counterfactual, "If Jones (who is not in this room) were in this room, he would be wearing green socks"; for the former statement is equally compatible with, "If Jones were in this room, it would be false that all the people in this room are wearing green socks."

The trouble comes in attempting to clarify the notion of a counterfactual conditional; for attempts to analyze it have not been successful. In particular, they cannot be interpreted, at least in any straightforward way, in terms of the usual logical notion of "if-then": for, since the antecedent (the "if . . ." part) of a counterfactual is always false, all counterfactuals would have to be true, even if they contradict one another. But as we have noted earlier, no clear alternative interpretation of the connective is available. On the other hand, efforts to stay with the logical "if-then," and yet uncover some stratagem to circumvent the difficulties just noted, have been forced, in their analyses of counterfactuals, to presuppose the very notion of lawlikeness that was supposed to be clarified by reference to counterfactuals! Such approaches are therefore involved in a vicious circle. Some further attempts to characterize the difference between lawlike and accidental generalizations are discussed in the selection by Arthur Pap.

IX. EXPLANATION AND THE ROLE OF MODELS

Another view illustrative of the widespread application of mathematical logic to problems of the philosophy of science is Hempel's conception of scientific explanation. An explanation, according to Hempel, may be either deductive or statistical; we will discuss briefly only the deductive variety. "Scientific explanation, prediction, and postdiction," writes Hempel, "all have the same logical character: they show that the fact under consideration can be inferred from certain other facts by means of specified general laws." Thus a sentence E is (deductively) explained if and only if it is deduced from a set of sentences including (1) a set L of general laws, and (2) a set C of statements of fact referring to "initial conditions." (Note that, since the explanation must contain law statements, Hempel's analysis depends on a prior analysis of the concept of "law.") Conversely, if E is explained by L and C, then E could have been predicted (or "postdicted") given L and C, and vice versa. For example, the statement, "The object I place in this liquid at time t (where t may be past, present, or future) dissolves," is explained by being deduced from (and could have been a prediction or postdiction made on the basis of) (1) the general law, "All sugar dissolves in water," and (2) the statements of initial conditions, "The object I place in this liquid at time t is sugar" and "This liquid is water."

Objections have frequently been raised against this view of explanation, even when it is restricted to scientific explanation and not held to be an analysis of the concept of "explanation" in general. Most of these objections fall into one of three main classes: (1) objections against the alleged symmetry between explanation and prediction; [14] (2) objections that not all cases of deductions from general laws and statements of initial conditions are explanations (indeed, Duhem claims that physical theories are not explanations at all); (3) objections that not all cases of explanation are cases of deduction from general laws and statements of initial conditions. We will here consider only one example of the third type of objection: namely, the argument that there is a type of explanation, in terms of "models," that, while common in the sciences, does not meet the Hempelian specifications.

There is no doubt that scientists often refer to such "modelistic" explanations: for example, the explanation of the chemical laws of combining proportions in terms of the atomic model; the explanation of the distribution of spectral lines by Bohr's planetary model of the atom; the explanation of diffraction patterns in terms of the wave model of light. But are such modelistic "explanations" really explanatory? Are models even essential elements of a scientific theory? Some thinkers, notably Duhem, have maintained that models have only a psychological function in science: they serve as mental crutches for feebles minds trying to visualize the point of mathematical formulas, which are the essence of scientific theories. They are thus "explanatory" only in the sense that they make such feeble minds feel at home with the rigorous mathematics of the theory, to which, logically, they are totally irrelevant. According to Pierre Duhem, models are not even literally descriptive—the atomic model does not really represent what is behind the scenes of chemical combination. And as for the analysis of scientific theories as interpreted

---

[14] Much of Toulmin's book, *Foresight and Understanding*, is an attack on "the predictivist view of explanation." In the selection reprinted in this anthology, however, Toulmin is more concerned with developing his own view of explanation. He draws attention to the ways in which "ideals of natural order" determine what is "normal" and what is a "phenomenon" calling for an explanation: "the cause or explanation of an event comes in question (i.e., it becomes a phenomenon) through seemingly deviating in this regular way."

axiomatic systems (above, Sec. VII), it did not even mention models; and an advocate of that analysis can consistently maintain that whatever real explanatory value there is to the model is exhausted by the logic and mathematics reflected by it, and that the model as an imaginative picture of how things really are only "explains" in the rather unimportant and irrelevant sense of making things seem familiar.

But are such views really fair representations of the role models have played, and perhaps must play, in the development and structure of science? The selection by Mary Hesse is one of a number of recent attempts to make a sober appraisal of the different senses of the term "model," and of the jobs performed in science by those factors. The results of such analyses clearly have important bearing not only on the validity of the Hempelian view of explanation, but also on that of the view that scientific theories are adequately represented as interpreted axiomatic systems.

X. INDUCTION AND SIMPLICITY

If the distinction between "theoretical" and "observational" is accepted and clarified, further problems arise with regard to the exact way in which observational facts are relevant to the acceptability or unacceptability of scientific statements.[15] Empirical evidence is often held to "confirm" (or "disconfirm") scientific laws or theories, and confirmation is said to be a matter of degree of evidential support; but the precise interpretation of the term "confirmation," of the conditions under which further evidence raises or lowers the degree of confirmation, and of the extent to which this degree of confirmation can be measured quantitatively, are all far from settled. Particularly with regard to the question of whether degree of confirmation can be measured quantitatively, the analysis of the concept of "probability" tends to occupy a central place, since it seems prima facie reasonable to suppose that the degree to which a scientific hypothesis is confirmed is the probability, on the basis of the evidence at hand, of its being true. These topics are discussed in the selection by Carnap. Other analyses of "probability," however, which are not connected with the notion of "degree of confirmation,"

---

[15] With regard to these questions, theses may be formulated that correspond closely to the first two theses concerning the relations between the meanings of theoretical and observational terms. A thesis (or set of alternative theses) paralleling Thesis III can also be formulated, but here special difficulties arise.

but rather with what Carnap calls "probability$_2$" (Carnap selection, Sec. II), have also been proposed.

Still others hold that the important work empirical facts perform with respect to laws and theories has to do not with confirmation, but with falsification. The selection by Kuhn is a criticism of both confirmation and falsification views of the acceptability or unacceptability of scientific theories and laws, as well as of operationalism. Some thinkers, again (including Duhem and Kuhn—see selections), maintain that no experiment or piece of observational evidence is "crucial" to the falsification of any single scientific statement—that there are always many alternative courses that may be taken in the face of counterevidence. Corresponding to this doctrine concerning the impossibility of a crucial experiment for the rejection or falsification of scientific laws or theories is a doctrine to the effect that any given body of empirical facts can be accounted for by (can confirm) more than one theory or law (perhaps an infinite number of them). Such views raise further problems: for if two or more theories are equally adequate in their accounts of the facts (are equally well confirmed by the facts), how is a choice to be made between the alternative theories? One much-discussed proposal is that considerations of "simplicity" enter in; but, again, the exact sense of "simplicity" relevant in such choices is problematic. The selection by Richard Rudner outlines a number of different notions of "simplicity" and some of the problems connected with them.

XI. LOGIC AND HISTORY OF SCIENCE

We have now reviewed some of the main problems discussed in the selections in this anthology. In particular, we have seen how those who approach the philosophy of science using mathematical logic as a model and a tool of analysis have tried to deal with those problems; and we have seen some of the criticisms to which their views have been subjected. Some philosophers, however, have felt that the troubles of that school go deeper, arising from an *over*use of logical ideas and techniques. For it does seem possible, for example, that the view that scientific theories are interpreted axiomatic systems may have blinded its adherents to many of the functions of those theories and their constituents. After all, the logician's treatment of science concentrates only on theories that have reached the high stage of development that must be achieved before they are ready for axiomatization; and therefore many of the good reasons that eventuated in that highly developed stage are ignored. Partly responsible for this omission is the view—a motto of "logical empiricism"—that "there is no logic of discovery." In some senses, this is true: we cannot substitute logic for genius. But it appears unlikely that no profit can be gained, in our attempt to understand what science is and does, by exploring the processes by which scientific concepts, laws, and theories are selected and refined to the point at which logical empiricism only begins to deal with them. This explains the recent interest displayed by such writers as Mary Hesse, Kuhn, and Toulmin (but Duhem long before) in the history of science: for a study of that subject can be expected to reveal not only "irrelevant" psychological and sociological causes of, but also very pertinent good reasons for, scientific development.

Again, even the highly developed scientific theories on which the axiomatic approach concentrates may be inadequately treated when looked upon as mere interpreted axiomatic systems. For the logician deals with those theories and their constituents as static, frozen in a logical mold; but perhaps there are more "dynamic" functions such an approach tends to make us overlook. Thus Hesse suggests that models function in the historical development of science as suggesting new avenues of investigation to the scientists; and Toulmin and Kuhn claim that "ideals of natural order" or "paradigms" play a role in determining not only the kinds of problems scientists are interested in, but also their standards for solving those problems and the very nature of the facts with which science deals.

Worse still, according to such critics, even where the axiomatic approach has called attention to some of the relations between scientific theories and between their constituents, it may well have produced a distorted picture of those workings. Thus Kuhn, in his critique of operationalist, verification, and falsification views of the acceptance or rejection of scientific theories, maintains that those views have misinterpreted the role of experimental fact in science. Some proponents of the "logical empiricist" approach have recently begun to confess that their treatment of scientific theories is only an "idealization"; but such an admission would seem to imply that what is needed now is an examination of the *differences* between scientific theories and interpreted axiomatic systems, and of any ways in which ignoring those differences may have adversely influenced some interpretations of science.

Many critics have felt that concentration on logical features has given to many logical empiricist discussions an air of irrelevance to science: pages may go by without any mention of scientific views (after all, those philosophers are not supposed to be interested primarily in any actual scientific views); and when such views are at last mentioned, they are brought in as examples to illustrate conclusions that, as far as can be determined from the discussion, were arrived at by purely technical arguments of mathematical logic, rather than by examination of concrete scientific cases. Is it any wonder that such discussions have come to be viewed with suspicion? The need has been felt more and more strongly that what is needed is a closer examination of actual scientific development and practice—of the jobs performed by terms and statements in their actual employment in science, and of the respects in which those jobs change and remain the same as science develops. This means a return to an examination of the "content" of science, of the ways in which uses of terms like "space," "time," "explanation," "cause," "law," which are employed in or in talking about scientific theories, are similar or different in different contexts, and how those uses are like, or depart from, the uses of corresponding terms in more ordinary (nonscientific) contexts.[16]

Certainly, even if these criticisms are correct, they should not be taken as recommending that the problems, methods, and results of the logical empiricist approach be completely abandoned as useless. As we have seen, those philosophers have made many issues remarkably precise, and viable alternatives to many of their interpretations are hard to come by. There is no guarantee that all or any of their difficulties will be removed or lessened by going beyond the use of logical techniques in the ways described above. But there is much promise that, at the very least, such new, broader approaches will reveal features of science that tended to be passed over by the logical treatment.

[16] It must not be supposed that such examinations have been missing from twentieth-century philosophy of science, even in the logical empiricist tradition; for disputes usually classified as "philosophical" have also arisen concerning questions of "content"—the methods and results of particular sciences (relativity, quantum mechanics, psychoanalysis); but those discussions, too, have tended to be dominated by an approach that concentrates on logical analysis and tends to ignore historical development.

PART I

Logical Approaches

CARL G. HEMPEL

The Theoretician's Dilemma:
A Study in the Logic of
Theory Construction

*Carl G. Hempel studied at Göttingen, Heidelberg, Vienna, and Berlin,
where he received his Ph.D. in 1934. He has taught at Chicago, City
College of New York, Queens College, Yale, and Harvard, and is now
Stuart Professor of Philosophy at Princeton. Among his many influential publications are:* Fundamentals of Concept Formation in Empirical
Science; *"Studies in the Logic of Confirmation"* (Mind, 1945); *"De-
ductive-Nomological vs. Statistical Explanation"* (Minnesota Studies in
the Philosophy of Science, *Vol. III, edited by H. Feigl and G. Maxwell);
and (with Paul Oppenheim)* "Studies in the Logic of Explanation"
(Philosophy of Science, 1948).

1. DEDUCTIVE AND INDUCTIVE SYSTEMATIZATION

Scientific explanation, prediction, and postdiction all have the
same logical character: they show that the fact under consideration
can be inferred from certain other facts by means of specified general laws. In the simplest case, this type of argument may be
schematized as a deductive inference of the following form:

From Carl G. Hempel, "The Theoretician's Dilemma," in *Minnesota Studies in
the Philosophy of Science*, Vol. II, ed. Herbert Feigl, Michael Scriven, and
Grover Maxwell, pp. 37–47, 49–52, 67–78, 87, *passim.* University of Minnesota
Press, Minneapolis. Copyright 1958 by the University of Minnesota.

$$C_1, C_2 \ldots C_k$$
$$L_1, L_2 \ldots L_r$$
$$E$$

(1.1)

Here, C_1, C_2, C_k are statements of particular occurrences (e.g., of the position and momenta of certain celestial bodies at a specified time), and L_1, $L_2 \ldots L_r$ are general laws (e.g., those of Newtonian mechanics); finally, E is a sentence stating whatever is being explained, predicted, or postdicted. And the argument has its intended force only if its conclusion, E, follows deductively from the premises. . . .

For these three types of scientific procedure, we will use the common term '*(deductive) systematization.*' More precisely, that term will be used to refer, first, to any argument of the form (1.1) that meets the requirements indicated above, no matter whether it serves as an explanation, a prediction, a postdiction, or in still some other capacity; second, to the procedure of establishing arguments of the kind just characterized.

So far, we have considered only those cases of explanation, prediction, and related procedures which can be construed as deductive arguments. There are many instances of scientific explanation and prediction, however, which do not fall into a strictly deductive pattern. For example, when Johnny comes down with the measles, this might be explained by pointing out that he caught the disease from his sister, who is just recovering from it. The particular antecedent facts here invoked are that of Johnny's exposure and, let us assume, the further fact that Johnny had not had the measles previously. But to connect these with the event to be explained, we cannot adduce a general law to the effect that under the specified circumstances, the measles is invariably transmitted to the exposed person: what can be asserted is only a high probability (in the sense of statistical frequency) of transmission. The same type of argument can be used also for predicting or postdicting the occurrence of a case of the measles. . . .

Explanations, predictions, and postdictions of the kind here illustrated differ from those previously discussed in two important respects: The laws invoked are of a different form, and the statement to be established does not follow deductively from the explanatory statements adduced. We will now consider these differences somewhat more closely.

The laws referred to in connection with the schema (1.1), such as the laws of Newtonian mechanics, are what we will call *statements of strictly universal form, or strictly universal statements*. A statement of this kind is an assertion—which may be true or false—to the effect that all cases which meet certain specified conditions will unexceptionally have such and such further characteristics. . . .

The laws invoked in the second type of explanatory and related arguments, on the other hand, are, as we will say, of *statistical form;* they are *statistical probability statements*. A statement of this kind is an assertion—which may be true or false—to the effect that for cases which meet conditions of a specified kind, the probability of having such and such further characteristics is so-and-so much.

To put the distinction in a nutshell: A strictly universal statement of the simplest kind has the form 'All cases of P are cases of Q'; a statistical probability statement of the simplest kind has the form 'The probability for a case of P to be a case of Q is r.' While the former implies an assertion about any particular instance of P— namely, that it is also an instance of Q—the latter implies no similar assertion concerning any particular instance of P or even concerning any finite set of such instances. This circumstance gives rise to the second distinctive characteristic mentioned above: the statement E describing the occurrence under explanation or prediction or post-diction (for example, Johnny's catching the measles) is not logically deducible from the explanatory statements adduced (for example, (C_1) Johnny was exposed to the measles; (C_2) Johnny had not previously had the measles; (L) For persons who have not previously had the measles and are exposed to it, the probability is .92 that they will contract the disease); rather, on the assumption that the explanatory statements adduced are true, it is very likely, though not certain, that E is true as well. This kind of argument, therefore, is inductive rather than strictly deductive in character; it calls for the acceptance of E on the basis of other statements which constitute only partial, if strongly supporting, grounds for it. An argument of this kind—no matter whether it is used for explanation, prediction, or postdiction, or for yet another purpose—will be called an *inductive systematization*. In particular, we will assume of an inductive systematization that the conclusion is not logically implied by the premises. Again, the procedure of establishing an argument of the kind just described will also be called inductive systematization. . . .

All the cases of scientific systematization we have considered share this characteristic: they make use of general laws or general principles either of strictly universal or of statistical form. These general laws have the function of establishing systematic connections among empirical facts in such a way that with their help some empirical occurrences may be inferred, by way of explanation, prediction, or postdiction, from other such occurrences. When, in an explanation, we say that the event described by E occurred "because" of the circumstances detailed in $C_1, C_2 \ldots C_k$, that phrase has significance if it can be construed as referring to general laws which render $C_1, C_2 \ldots C_k$ relevant to E in the sense that, granted the truth of the former, they make the truth of the latter either certain (as in a deductive systematization) or inductively probable (as in an inductive systematization). It is for this reason that the establishment of general laws is of crucial importance in the empirical sciences.

2. OBSERVABLES AND THEORETICAL ENTITIES

Scientific systematization is ultimately aimed at establishing explanatory and predictive order among the bewilderingly complex "data" of our experience, the phenomena that can be directly "observed" by us. It is a remarkable fact, therefore, that the greatest advances in scientific systematization have not been accomplished by means of laws referring explicitly to *observables*, i.e., to things and events which are ascertainable by direct observation, but rather by means of laws that speak of various *hypothetical, or theoretical, entities*, i.e., presumptive objects, events, and attributes which cannot be perceived or otherwise directly observed by us.

For a fuller discussion of this point, it will be helpful to refer to the familiar distinction between two levels of scientific systematization: the level of *empirical generalization*, and the level of *theory formation*. The early stages in the development of a scientific discipline usually belong to the former level, which is characterized by the search for laws (of universal or statistical form) which establish connections among the directly observable aspects of the subject matter under study. The more advanced stages belong to the second level, where research is aimed at comprehensive laws, in terms of hypothetical entities, which will account for the uniformities established on the first level. On the first level, we find everyday physical generalizations such as 'Where there is light there is heat,' 'Iron rusts in damp air,' 'Wood floats on water, iron sinks in it'; but we might assign to it also such more precise quantitative laws as Galileo's, Kepler's, Hooke's, and Snell's laws, as well as botanical and zoological generalizations about the concomitance of certain observable anatomical, physical, functional, and other characteristics in the members of a given species; generalizations in psychology that assert correlations among diverse observable aspects of learning, of perception, and so forth; and various descriptive generalizations in economics, sociology, and anthropology. All these generalizations, whether of strictly universal or of statistical form, purport to express regular connections among directly observable phenomena, and they lend themselves, therefore, to explanatory, predictive, and postdictive use.

On the second level, we encounter general statements that refer to electric, magnetic, and gravitational fields, to molecules, atoms, and a variety of subatomic particles; or to ego, id, superego, libido, sublimation, fixation, and transference; or to various not directly observable entities invoked in recent learning theories.

In accordance with the distinction here made, we will assume that the (extra-logical) vocabulary of empirical science, or of any of its branches, is divided into two classes: *observational terms* and *theoretical terms*. In regard to an observational term it is possible, under suitable circumstances, to decide by means of direct observation whether the term does or does not apply to a given situation.

Observation may here be construed so broadly as to include not only perception, but also sensation and introspection; or it may be limited to the perception of what in principle is publicly ascertainable, i.e., perceivable also by others. The subsequent discussion will be independent of how narrowly or how liberally the notion of observation is construed. . . .

Theoretical terms, on the other hand, usually purport to refer to not directly observable entities and their characteristics; they function, in a manner soon to be examined more closely, in scientific theories intended to explain empirical generalizations.

The preceding characterization of the two vocabularies is obviously vague; it offers no precise criterion by means of which any scientific term may be unequivocally classified as an observational term or as a theoretical one. But no such precise criterion is needed here; the questions to be examined in this essay are independent of precisely where the dividing line between the terms of the observational and the theoretical vocabularies is drawn.

3. WHY THEORETICAL TERMS?

The use of theoretical terms in science gives rise to a perplexing problem: Why should science resort to the assumption of hypothetical entities when it is interested in establishing predictive and explanatory connections among observables? Would it not be sufficient for the purpose, and much less extravagant at that, to search for a system of general laws mentioning only observables, and thus expressed in terms of the observational vocabulary alone?

Many general statements in terms of observables have indeed been formulated; they constitute the empirical generalizations mentioned in the preceding section. But, vexingly, many, if not all, of them suffer from definite shortcomings: they usually have a rather limited range of application; and even within that range, they have exceptions, so that actually they are not true general statements. Take, for example, one of our earlier illustrations of an empirical generalization:

(3.1)   Wood floats on water; iron sinks in it.

This statement has a narrow range of application in the sense that it refers only to wooden and iron objects and concerns their floating behavior only in regard to water. And, what is even more important, it has exceptions: certain kinds of wood will sink in water, and a hollow iron sphere of suitable dimensions will float on it.

As the history of science shows, flaws of this kind can often be remedied by attributing to the phenomena under study certain further constituents or characteristics which, though not open to direct observation, are connected in specified ways with the observable aspects of the subject matter under investigation, and which make it possible to establish systematic connections among the latter. By way of illustration—though it is admittedly an oversimplified one—consider the sentence (3.1). A much more satisfactory generalization is obtained by means of the concept of the specific gravity of a body x, which is definable as the quotient of its weight and its volume:

(3.2)   Def.: $s(x) = w(x)/v(x)$

Let us assume that w and v have been characterized operationally, i.e., in terms of the directly observable outcomes of specified measuring procedures, and that therefore they are counted among the observables. Then s, as determined by (3.1), might be viewed as a characteristic that is less directly observable; and, just for the sake of obtaining a simple illustration, we will classify s as a hypothetical entity. For s, we may now state the following generalization, which is a corollary of the principle of Archimedes:

(3.3)   A solid body floats on a liquid if its specific gravity is less than that of the liquid.

This statement avoids, first of all, the exceptions we noted above as refuting (3.1): it predicts correctly the behavior of a piece of heavy wood and of a hollow iron sphere. Moreover, it has a much wider scope: it refers to any kind of solid object and concerns its floating behavior in regard to any liquid. Even the new generalization has certain limitations, of course, and thus invites further improvement. But instead of pursuing this process, let us now examine more closely the way in which a systematic connection among observables is achieved, in our illustration, by the law (3.3), which involves a detour through the domain of unobservables.

Suppose that we wish to predict whether a certain solid object b will float on a given body l of liquid. We will then first have to ascertain, by appropriate operational procedure, the weight and the volume of b and l. Let the results of these measurements be expressed by the following four statements O_1, O_2, O_3, O_4:

(3.4) $(O_1)\ w(b) = w_1;\ (O_2)\ v(b) = v_1$
$(O_3)\ w(l) = w_2;\ (O_4)\ v(l) = v_2$

where w_1, w_2, v_1, v_2, are certain positive real numbers. By means of the definition (3.2), we can infer, from (3.4), the specific gravities of b and l:

(3.5) $s(b) = w_1/v_1;\ s(l) = w_2/v_2$

Suppose now that the first of these values is less than the second; then (3.4), via (3.5) implies that

(3.6) $s(b) < s(l)$

By means of the law (3.3), we can now infer that

(3.7)   b floats on l

This sentence will also be called O_5. The sentences O_1, O_2, O_3, O_4, O_5 then share the characteristic that they are expressed entirely in terms of the observational vocabulary; for on our assumption, 'w' and 'v' are observational terms, and so are 'b' and 'l', which name certain observable bodies; finally, 'floats on' is an observational term because under suitable circumstances, direct observation will show whether a given observable object floats on a given observable liquid. On the other hand, the sentences (3.2), (3.3), (3.5), and (3.6) lack that characteristic, for they all contain the term 's', which, in our illustration, belongs to the theoretical vocabulary.

The systematic transition from the "observational data" listed in (3.4) to the prediction (3.7) of an observable phenomenon is schematized in the accompanying diagram. Here, an arrow represents a deductive inference; mention, above an arrow, of a further

$$(3.8) \quad \left.\begin{array}{l} O_1 \\ O_2 \end{array}\right\} \xrightarrow{(3.2)} s(b) = v_1/w_1 \\ \left.\begin{array}{l} O_3 \\ O_4 \end{array}\right\} \xrightarrow{(3.2)} s(l) = v_2/w_2 \right\} \xrightarrow{\quad} s(b) < s(l) \xrightarrow{(3.9)} O_5$$

Data described in terms of observables	Systematic connection effected by statements making reference to non-observables	Prediction in terms of observables

sentence indicates that the deduction is effected by means of that sentence, i.e., that the conclusion stated at the right end follows logically from the premises listed at the left, taken in conjunction with the sentence mentioned above the arrow. Note that the argument just considered illustrates the schema (1.1), with O_1, O_2, O_3, O_4 constituting the statements of particular facts, the sentences (3.2) and (3.3) taking the place of the general laws, and O_5 that of E.

Thus, the assumption of non-observable entities serves the purposes of systematization: it provides connections among observables in the form of laws containing theoretical terms, and this detour via the domain of hypothetical entities offers certain advantages, some of which were indicated above.

In the case of our illustration, however, brief reflection will show that the advantages obtained by the "theoretical detour" could just as well have been obtained without ever resorting to the use of a theoretical term. Indeed, by virtue of the definition (3.2), the law (3.3) can be restated as follows:

(3.3′) A solid body floats on a liquid if the quotient of its weight and its volume is less than the corresponding quotient for the liquid.

This alternative version clearly shares the advantages we found (3.3) to have over the crude generalization (3.1); and, of course, it permits the deductive transition from O_1, O_2, O_3, O_4 to O_5 just as well as does (3.3) in conjunction with (3.2).

The question arises therefore whether the systematization achieved by general principles containing theoretical terms can always be duplicated by means of general statements couched exclusively in observational terms. To prepare for an examination of this important problem, we must first consider more closely the form and function of a scientific theory.

4. STRUCTURE AND INTERPRETATION OF A THEORY

Formally, a scientific theory may be considered as a set of sentences expressed in terms of a specific vocabulary. The vocabulary, V_T, of a theory T will be understood to consist of the extralogical terms of T, i.e., those which do not belong to the vocabulary of pure logic. Usually, some of the terms of V are defined by means of others; but, on pain of a circle or an infinite regress, not all the terms of V can be so defined. Hence, V may be assumed to be divided into two subsets: *primitive terms*—those for which no definition is specified—and *defined terms*. Analogously, many of the sentences of a theory are derivable from others by means of the principles of deductive logic (and of the definitions of the defined terms); but, on pain of a vicious circle or an infinite regress in the deduction, not all of the theoretical sentences can be thus established. Hence, the set of sentences asserted by T falls into two subsets: *primitive sentences*, or *postulates* (also called *axioms*), and *derivative sentences*, or *theorems*. Henceforth, we will assume that theories are given in the form of axiomatized systems as here described; i.e., by listing, first, the primitive and the derivative terms and the definitions for the latter, second, the postulates. In addition, the theory will always be thought of as formulated within a linguistic framework of a clearly specified logical structure, which determines, in particular, the rules of deductive inference. . . .

If the primitive terms and the postulates of an axiomatized system have been specified, then the proof of theorems, i.e., the derivation of further sentences from the primitive ones—can be carried out by means of the purely formal canons of deductive logic, and thus, without any reference to the meanings of the terms and sentences at hand; indeed, for the deductive development of an axiomatized system, no meanings need be assigned at all to its expressions, primitive or derived.

However, a deductive system can function as a theory in empirical science only if it has been given an *interpretation* by reference to empirical phenomena. We may think of such interpretation as being effected by the specification of a set of *interpretative sentences,* which connect certain terms of the theoretical vocabulary with observational terms. The character of these sentences will be examined in considerable detail in subsequent sections; at present may be mentioned, merely as an example, that interpretative sentences might take the form of so-called operational definitions, i.e., of statements specifying the meanings of theoretical terms with the help of observational ones; of special importance among these are rules for the measurement of theoretical quantities by reference to observable responses of measuring instruments or other indicators. . . .

5. THE THEORETICIAN'S DILEMMA

The preceding account of the function of theories raises anew the problem encountered in section 3, namely, whether the theoretical detour, through a domain of not directly observable things, events, or characteristics cannot be entirely avoided. Assume, for example, that—as will often be the case—the interpretative sentences as well as the laws asserted by the theory have the form of equations which connect certain expressions in terms of theoretical quantities either with other such expressions, or with expressions in terms of observable quantities. Then the problem can be stated in Hull's succinct formulation: "If you have a secure equational linkage extending from the antecedent observable conditions through to the consequent observable conditions, why, even though to do so might not be positively pernicious, use several equations where one would do?"[1] . . .

The conclusion suggested by these arguments might be called *the paradox of theorizing.* It asserts that if the terms and the general

---

[1] C. L. Hull, "The Problem of Intervening Variables in Molar Behavior Theory," *Psychological Review,* Vol. 50 (1943), p. 284. Reprinted in M. H. Marx (ed.), *Psychological Theory.* The Macmillan Company, New York, 1951.

principles of a scientific theory serve their purpose, i.e., if they establish definite connections among observable phenomena, then they can be dispensed with since any chain of laws and interpretative statements establishing such a connection should then be replaceable by a law which directly links observational antecedents to observational consequents.

By adding to this crucial thesis two further statements which are obviously true, we obtain the premises for an argument in the classical form of a dilemma:

(5.1) If the terms and principles of a theory serve their purpose they are unnecessary, as just pointed out, and if they don't serve their purpose they are surely unnecessary. But given any theory, its terms and principles either serve their purpose or they don't. Hence, the terms and principles of any theory are unnecessary.

This argument, whose conclusion accords well with the views of extreme methodological behaviorists in psychology, will be called the *theoretician's dilemma*.

However, before yielding to glee or to gloom over the outcome of this argument, it will be well to remember that the considerations adduced so far in support of the crucial first premise were formulated rather sketchily. In order to form a more careful judgment on the issue, it will therefore be necessary to inquire whether the sketch can be filled in so as to yield a cogent argument. To this task we now turn.

6. OPERATIONAL DEFINITIONS AND REDUCTION SENTENCES

It will be well to begin by considering more closely the character of interpretative sentences. In the simplest case, such a sentence could be an *explicit definition* of a theoretical expression in terms of observational ones, as illustrated by (3.2). In this case, the theoretical term is unnecessary in the strong sense that it can always be avoided in favor of an observational expression, its definiens. If all the primitives of a theory T are thus defined, then clearly T can be stated entirely in observational terms, and all its general principles will indeed be laws that directly connect observables with observables.

This would be true, in particular, of any theory that meets the standards of operationism in the narrow sense that each of its terms is introduced by an explicit definition which states an observable response whose occurrence is necessary and sufficient, under specified observable test conditions, for the applicability of the term in question. Suppose, for example, that the theoretical term is a one-place predicate, or property term, 'Q'. Then an operational definition of the kind just mentioned would take the form

$$(6.1) \qquad\qquad \text{Def. } Qx \equiv (Cx \supset Ex)$$

i.e., an object x has (by definition) the property Q if and only if it is such that if it is under test conditions of kind C, then it exhibits an effect, or response of kind E. Tolman's definition of expectancy of food provides an illustration: "When we assert that a rat expects food at L, what we assert is that *if* (1) he is deprived of food, (2) he has been trained on path P, (3) he is now put on path P, (4) path P is now blocked, and (5) there are other paths which lead away from path P, one of which points directly to location L, *then* he will run down the path which points directly to location L." [2] We can obtain this formulation by replacing, in (6.1), 'Qx' by 'rat x expects food at location L,' 'Cx' by the conjunction of the conditions (1), (2), (3), (4), (5) for rat x, and 'Ex' by 'x runs down the path which points directly to location L.'

However, as has been shown by Carnap in a now classical argument,[3] this manner of defining scientific terms, no matter how natural it may seem, encounters a serious difficulty. For on the standard extensional interpretation, a conditional sentence, such as the definiens in (6.1), is false only if its antecedent is true and its consequent false. Hence, for any object which does not satisfy the test conditions C, and for which therefore the antecedent of the definiens is false, the definiens as a whole is true; consequently, such an object will be assigned the property Q. In terms of our illustration: of any rat not exposed to the conditions (1)–(5) just stated, we would have to say that he expected food at L—no matter what kind of behavior the rat might exhibit.

[2] E. C. Tolman, B. F. Ritchie, and D. Kalish, "Studies in Spatial Learning. I. Orientation and the Short-Cut," *Journal of Experimental Psychology*, Vol. 36 (1946), p. 15.

[3] R. Carnap, "Testability and Meaning," *Philosophy of Science*, 1936–37, Sec. 4; reprinted as a monograph by Whitlock's Inc., New Haven, Conn., 1950. Excerpts are contained in H. Feigl and M. Brodbeck (eds.), *Readings in the Philosophy of Science*. Appleton-Century-Crofts, New York, 1953.

One way out of this difficulty is suggested by the following consideration. In saying that a given rat expects food at L, we intend to attribute to the animal a state or a disposition which, under circumstances (1)–(5), will *cause* the rat to run down the path pointing directly to L; hence, in a proper operational definition, E must be tied to C nomologically, i.e., by virtue of general laws of the kind expressing causal connections. The extensional "if . . . then . . .'[4]—which requires neither logical nor nomological necessity of connection—would therefore have to be replaced in (6.1) by a stricter, nomological counterpart that might be worded perhaps as "if . . . then, with causal necessity, . . .' However, the ideas of law and of causal or nomological necessity as here invoked are not clear enough at present to make this approach seem promising.

Carnap has proposed an alternative way of meeting the difficulty encountered by definitions of the form (6.1); it consists in providing a partial rather than a complete specification of meaning for 'Q'. This is done by means of so-called reduction sentences; in the simplest case, (6.1) would be replaced by the following *bilateral reduction sentence:*

$$(6.2) \qquad\qquad Cx \supset (Qx \equiv Ex)$$

i.e., if an object is under test conditions of kind C, then it has the property Q if and only if it exhibits a response of kind E. Here, the use of extensional connectives no longer has the undesirable aspects it exhibited in (6.1); if an object is not under test conditions C, then the entire formula (6.2) is true of it, but this implies nothing as to whether the object does, or does not, have the property Q. On the other hand, while (6.1) offers a full explicit definition of 'Q', (6.2) specifies the meaning of 'Q' only partly, namely, for just those objects that meet condition C; for those which don't, the meaning of 'Q' is left unspecified. In our illustration, for example, (6.2) would specify the meaning of 'x expects food at L' only for rats that meet conditions (1)–(5); for them, running down the path which pointed to L would be a necessary and sufficient condition of food expectancy. In reference to rats that don't meet the test conditions (1)–(5), the meaning of 'x expects food at L' would be

---

[4] "If-then" (in the logician's sense) is *extensional* in that it connects propositions in such a way that the truth or falsity of the resulting compound is determined by the truth or falsity of the components; *cf. Introduction,* Sec. IV.—Ed.

left open; it could be further specified subsequently by means of additional reduction sentences. . . .

As this example vividly illustrates, reduction sentences offer an excellent way of formulating precisely the intent of operational definitions. By construing the latter as merely partial specifications of meaning, this approach treats theoretical concepts as "open"; and the provision for a set of different, and mutually supplementary, reduction sentences for a given term reflects the availability, for most theoretical terms, of different operational criteria of application, pertaining to different contexts.

It should be noted, however, that while an analysis in terms of reduction sentences construes theoretical terms as not fully defined by reference to observables, it does not prove that a full explicit definition in observational terms *cannot* be achieved for theoretical expressions. . . .

7. ON THE DEFINABILITY OF THEORETICAL TERMS BY MEANS OF AN OBSERVATIONAL VOCABULARY

. . . A number of writers have taken the position that even if in principle theoretical terms could be avoided in favor of observational ones, it would be practically impossible or—what is more serious—methodologically disadvantageous or even stultifying to do so.

There is, for example, the answer given by Tolman and by Spence to the problem considered by Hull, which was mentioned in section 5 above: if intervening theoretical variables can establish a secure linkage between antecedent and consequent observable conditions, why should we not use just one functional connection that directly links antecedents and consequents? Spence adduces as one reason, also suggested by Tolman,[5] the following consideration: the mathematical function required to express the connection will be so complex that it is humanly impossible to conceive of it all at once; we can arrive at it only by breaking it down into a sequence of simpler functional connections, mediated by intervening variables. This

---

[5] E. C. Tolman, "Operational Behaviorism and Current Trends in Psychology," *Proceedings of the 25th Anniversary Celebration of the Inauguration of Graduate Study*, Los Angeles, 1936, p. 89; K. W. Spence, "The Nature of Theory Construction in Contemporary Psychology," *Psychological Review*, Vol. 51 (1944), p. 65n. Both of these papers are reprinted in Marx, *op. cit.*

argument, then, attributes to the introduction of unobservable theoretical entities an important practical role in the context of discovering interdependencies among observables, and presumably also in the context of actually performing the calculations required for the explanation or prediction of specific occurrences on the basis of those interdependencies.

An important methodological function is attributed to hypothetical entities in an interesting passage of Hull's essay on intervening variables in molar behavior theory. The crucial point of Hull's argument is this: Suppose that in order to explain or predict the response of a subject in a given situation, we attribute to the subject, at the time t_1 of his response, a certain habit strength, which has the status of a hypothetical entity. That strength is, in Hull's theory, "merely a quantitative representation of the perseverative after-effects" of certain earlier observable events, such as observable stimuli received in temporally remote learning situations. Consequently, if reference to the hypothetical entity, habit strength, were avoided by linking the subject's observable response at t_1 directly to the observable stimuli received earlier then we would be invoking, as causal determinants for the response, certain observable events which at the time of the response, have long ceased to exist. And Hull rejects this notion, apparently inevitable when intervening hypothetical entities are eschewed, of causal action over a temporal distance: "it is hard to believe that an event such as stimulation in a remote learning situation can be causally active long after it has ceased to act on the receptors. I fully agree with Lewin that all the factors alleged to be causally influential in the determination of any other event must be in existence at the time of such causal action." [6] The hypothetical factor represented by the habit strength of the subject at the time t_1 of his response permits an explanation that accords with this principle.

Though the concluding part of the passage just quoted sounds quite metaphysical, the basic import of Hull's argument is methodological. . . . Such spatio-temporally continuous theories appear to recommend themselves for at least two reasons: first, they possess a certain formal simplicity, which at present can hardly be characterized in precise terms, but which is reflected, for example, in the possibility of using the powerful and elegant mathematical machinery of the calculus for the deduction, from the postulates of the

[6] Hull, *op. cit.*, p. 285.

theory, of explanatory and predictive connections among particular occurrences. And second, as was mentioned in section 3, the past development of empirical science seems to show that explanatory and predictive principles asserting discontinuous connections among (spatio-temporally separated) observable events are likely to be found to have limited scope and various kinds of exceptions. The use of theories in terms of hypothetical entities frequently makes it possible to account for such exceptions by means of suitable assumptions concerning the hypothetical entities involved.

Another, more general, argument that must be considered here has been developed in a lucid and precise manner by Braithwaite. . . . Braithwaite's main contention is that "theoretical terms can only be defined by means of observable properties on condition that the theory cannot be adapted properly to apply to new situations." [7] . . . Braithwaite's claim can be adequately illustrated, it seems, by the following example: suppose that the term 'temperature' is interpreted, at a certain stage of scientific research, only by reference to the readings of a mercury thermometer. If this observational criterion is taken as just a partial interpretation (namely as a sufficient but not necessary condition), then the possibility is left open of adding further partial interpretations, by reference to other thermometrical substances which are usable above the boiling point or below the freezing point of mercury; and this permits a vast increase in the range of application of such laws as those connecting the temperature of a metal rod with its length or with its electric resistance, or the temperature of a gas with its pressure or its volume. If, however, the original criterion is given the status of a complete definiens, then the theory is not capable of such expansion; rather, the original definition has to be abandoned in favor of another one, which is incompatible with the first. . . .

However, the argument here outlined can hardly be said to establish what is claimed, namely that "A theory which it is hoped may be expanded in the future to explain more generalizations than it was originally designed to explain must allow more freedom to its theoretical terms than would be given them were they to be logical constructions out of observable entities" [8] (and thus defined in terms of the latter). For clearly, the procedure of expanding a

[7] R. B. Braithwaite, *Scientific Explanation*. Cambridge University Press, Cambridge, England, 1953, p. 76.

[8] Braithwaite, *op. cit.*, p. 76.

theory at the cost of changing the definitions of some theoretical terms is not logically faulty; nor can it even be said to be difficult or inconvenient for the scientist, for the problem at hand is rather one for the methodologist or the logician, who seeks to give a clear "explication" or "logical reconstruction" of the changes occurring in an expansion of a given theory. And in the type of case discussed by Braithwaite, for example, this can be done in alternative ways— either in terms of additions to the original partial interpretation, or in terms of a total change of definition for some theoretical expressions. And if it is held that this latter method constitutes, not an expansion of the original theory, but a transition to a new one, this would raise more a terminological question than a methodological objection. . . .

The survey made in the present section has yielded no conclusive argument for or against the possibility of explicitly defining all theoretical terms of empirical science by means of a purely observational vocabulary; and in fact we have found strong reasons to doubt that any argument can settle the question once and for all. . . .

8. INTERPRETATIVE SYSTEMS

. . . Reduction sentences, as we saw earlier, are very well suited for the formulation of operational criteria of application as partial definitions. But they are subject to rather severe limitations as to logical form and thus do not seem sufficient to provide a satisfactory general schema for the partial interpretation of theoretical terms. A broader view of interpretation is suggested by Campbell's conception of a physical theory as consisting of a "hypothesis," represented by a set of sentences in theoretical terms, and a "dictionary," which relates the latter to concepts of experimental physics (which must be interconnected by empirical laws).[9] In contrast to the standard conception of a dictionary, Campbell's dictionary is assumed to contain, not definitions for the theoretical terms, but statements to the effect that a theoretical sentence of a certain kind is true if and only if a corresponding empirical sentence of a specified kind is true. Thus, rather than definitions, the dictionary provides rules of translation; and partial rules at that, for no claim is made that a translation must be specified for each theoretical statement or for each empirical statement. . . .

[9] N. R. Campbell, *Physics: The Elements*. Dover Press, New York, 1920, Ch. VI.

The statements in Campbell's dictionary evidently do not have the character of reduction sentences; they might be formulated, however, as biconditionals in which a sentence in theoretical terms is connected, by an "if and only if" clause, with a sentence in observational terms.

In other contexts, neither reduction sentences nor such biconditionals seem to be adequate. . . .

. . . In order to obtain a general concept of partial interpretation, we will now admit as interpretative statements any sentences, of whatever logical form, which contain theoretical and observational terms. On the assumption that the theoretical and observational statements of empirical science are formulated within a specified logical framework, this idea can be stated more precisely and explicitly as follows:

(8.5) Let T be a theory *characterized by* a set of postulates in terms of a finite *theoretical vocabulary* V_T, and let V_B be a second set of extra-logical terms, to be called the *basic vocabulary*, which shares no term with V_T. By an *interpretative system* for T with the basis V_B we will then understand a set J of sentences which (i) is finite, (ii) is logically compatible with T, (iii) contains no extra-logical term that is not contained in V_T or V_B, (iv) contains every element of V_T and V_B essentially, i.e., it is not logically equivalent to some set of sentences in which some term of V_T or V_B does not occur at all.

In applying the concept here defined to the analysis of scientific theories, we will have to assume, of course, that V_B consists of terms which are antecedently understood. They might be observational terms, in the somewhat vague sense explained earlier; but we need not insist on this. . . .

Interpretative systems as just defined include as special cases all the types of interpretation we considered earlier, namely, interpretation by explicit definitions for all theoretical terms, by chains of reduction sentences, by biconditional translation statements in the sense of Campbell's dictionary, and by generalized reduction sentences of the form (8.4); but of course they also allow for interpretative statements in a large variety of other forms.

Interpretative systems have the same two characteristics which distinguish chains of reduction sentences from chains of definitions:

First, an interpretative system normally effects only a partial interpretation of the terms in V_T; i.e., it does not lay down (by explicit statement or by logical implication), for every term in V_T, a necessary and sufficient condition of application in terms of V_B. Second, like a chain of reduction sentences for a given theoretical term, an interpretative system will normally not be purely stipulative in character, but will imply certain statements in terms of V_B alone which are not logical truths, and which, on the conception of V_B as consisting of antecedently understood empirical terms, may be viewed as expressing empirical assertions. Thus, here again, we find a combination of the stipulative and the descriptive use of language.

But, to turn to a third point of comparison, an interpretative system need not provide an interpretation—complete or incomplete —for each term in V_T individually. In this respect it differs from a set of definitions, which specifies for each term a necessary and sufficient condition, and from a set of reduction sentences, which provides for each term a necessary and a—usually different—sufficient condition. It is quite possible that an interpretative system provides, for some or even all of the terms in V_T, no necessary or no sufficient condition in terms of V_B, or indeed neither of the two; instead, it might specify, by explicit statement or by logical implication, sufficient or necessary conditions in terms of V_B only for certain expressions containing several terms of V_T—for example, in the manner of Campbell's dictionary.

As a rule, therefore, when a theory T is interpreted by an interpretative system J, the theoretical terms are not dispensable in the narrow sense of eliminability from all contexts, in favor of defining expressions in terms of V_B. Nor are they generally dispensable in the sense that J provides, for every sentence H that can be formed by means of V_T, a "translation" into terms of V_B, i.e., a sentence O in terms of V_B such that the biconditional $H \equiv O$ is logically deducible from J.

Are theoretical terms, then, altogether indispensable on this broad conception of interpretation so that the "paradox of theorizing" formulated in section 5 no longer applies to them? We consider this question in the next section.

9. FUNCTIONAL REPLACEABILITY OF THEORETICAL TERMS

The systematizing function of a theory T, as interpreted by an interpretative system J will consist in permitting inferences from given "data" in terms of V_B to certain other (e.g., predictive) statements in terms of V_B.

[Hempel proceeds to show that whatever systematization is achieved among the V_B-sentences can be accomplished by T together with J. The postulates of T together with the sentences of J can therefore be considered to be the postulates of a system T′ which Hempel calls an *interpreted theory*. Its vocabulary $V_{T′}$ is the sum of V_T and V_B. He proves that T′ achieves exactly the same deductive connections among V_B-sentences as does the set of all those theorems of T′ which are expressible in terms of V_B alone—these he calls the set of V_B-theorems or V_B-consequences of T′, and designates it by '$O_{T′}$.' Thus the deductive systematization achieved by T′ is exactly that achieved by $O_{T′}$, which contains no theoretical terms at all, and the theoretical terms can in principle be dispensed with.—Ed.]

But $O_{T′}$ is normally an unwieldy infinite set of statements, and the question arises therefore whether there is some generally applicable method of making it more manageable and perspicuous by putting it into the form of an axiomatized theoretical system T′$_B$, which would be formulated in terms of V_B alone. A theorem in formal logic which was recently proved by Craig shows that this is indeed the case, provided only that T′ satisfies certain extremely liberal and unconfining conditions.[10]

Thus Craig's theorem has a definite bearing upon the problems raised by the "paradox of theorizing," which was stated in section 5 in somewhat vague terms. The theorem at hand points out one way in which the "paradox" can be given a clear and precise interpretation and a rigorous proof: It shows that for any theory T′ using both theoretical terms and non-theoretical, previously understood ones, there exists, under certain very widely satisfied conditions, an axiomatized theoretical system T′$_B$ which uses only the non-theoretical terms of T′ and yet is functionally equivalent with T′ in the sense of effecting, among the sentences expressible in the non-theoretical vocabulary, exactly the same deductive connections as T′.

Should empirical science then avail itself of this method and replace all its theories involving assumptions about hypothetical entities by functionally equivalent theoretical systems couched ex-

[10] A non-technical discussion of these results is given in W. Craig, "Replacement of Auxiliary Expressions," *Philosophical Review,* Vol. 65 (1956), pp. 38–55.

clusively in terms which have direct observational reference or which are, at any rate, clearly understood? There are various reasons which make this inadvisable in consideration of the objectives of scientific theorizing.

To begin with, let us consider the general character of Craig's method. Disregarding many subtle points of detail, the procedure may be described as follows: By means of a constructive procedure, Craig arranges all the V_B-theorems of T' in a sequence. This sequence is highly redundant, for it contains, for any sentence occurring in it, also all its logical equivalents (as far as they are expressible in V_B). Craig prescribes a procedure for eliminating many, though not even all, of these duplications. The remaining sequence therefore still contains each V_B-theorem of T' in at least one of its various equivalent formulations. Finally, all the sentences in this remaining sequence are made postulates of T'_B. Thus, the set of V_B-theorems of T' is "axiomatized" in T'_B only in a rather Pickwickian sense, namely by making every sentence of the set, in some of its many equivalent formulations, a postulate of T'_B; whereas normally, the axiomatization of a set of sentences is intended to select as postulates just a small subset from which the rest can then be logically derived as theorems. In this manner, the axiomatization expresses the content of the whole set "in a form which is psychologically or mathematically more perspicuous." [11] And since Craig's method in effect includes all sentences that are to be axiomatized among the postulates of T'_B, the latter, as Craig himself puts it, "fail to simplify or to provide genuine insight." [12]

The loss in simplicity which results from discarding the theoretical terms of T' is reflected in the circumstance that the set of postulates which Craig's method yields for T'_B is always infinite. Even in cases where actually there exists some finite subset of $O_{T'}$ of V_B-theorems of T' from which all the rest can be deduced, Craig's procedure will not yield such a subset: that is the price of the universal applicability of Craig's method.

Now there are cases where an infinity of postulates may not be excessively unwieldy; notably when the axioms are specified by means of axiom-schemata, i.e., by stipulations to the effect that any sentence that has one of a finite number of specified forms (such as 'x = x', for example) is to count as an axiom. But the manner in

[11] Craig, *op. cit.*, p. 49.
[12] *Ibid.*

which the axioms, or postulates, of T'_B are specified by Craig's method is vastly more intricate, and the resulting system would be practically unmanageable—to say nothing of the loss in the heuristic fertility and suggestiveness which results from the elimination of the theoretical concepts and hypotheses. For empirical science, therefore, this method of dispensing with theoretical expressions would be quite unsatisfactory. . . .

When scientists or methodologists claim that the theoretical terms of a given theory refer to entities which have an existence of their own, which are essential constituents or aspects of the world we live in, then, no matter what individual connotations they may connect with this assertion, the reasons they could adduce in support of it seem clearly to lie in the fact that those terms function in a well-confirmed theory which effects an economical systematization, both deductive and inductive, of a large class of particular facts and empirical generalizations, and which is heuristically fertile in suggesting further questions and new hypotheses. And as far as suitability for inductive systematization, along with economy and heuristic fertility, are considered essential characteristics of a scientific theory, theoretical terms cannot be replaced without serious loss by formulations in terms of observables only: the theoretician's dilemma, whose conclusion asserts the contrary, starts with a false premise.

ARTHUR PAP

What Is a Law of Nature?

Arthur Pap was born in Zürich, Switzerland, and emigrated to New York in 1941. He received a doctorate in philosophy from Columbia in 1946, and taught at Chicago, City College of New York, Oregon, Vienna, Lehigh, and Yale, where he remained until his death in 1959 at the age of thirty-eight. Besides his Introduction to the Philosophy of Science, *his best-known books are* Elements of Analytic Philosophy *and* Semantics and Necessary Truth.

A. LAWLIKE GENERALIZATIONS AND COUNTERFACTUAL INFERENCE

In the last two chapters we have attempted to elucidate the causal and counterfactual meaning of "if-then." We have argued, in the spirit of Hume, that a belief in the existence of a logically contingent law, whether strict or probabilistic, is involved in counterfactual conditionals such as "If the match were struck (with the right amount of force), it would light." [1] But what exactly is the if-then connection asserted by a lawlike generalization, i.e., a generalization that, if assumed to be true, is said to express a law of nature? Causal implication, we said, is stronger than material implication because it rules certain kinds of events out as *impossible;* it does not just deny their actual occurrence. On the other hand, it is weaker than analytic implication. [2] Can we say anything more positive about the relevant senses of "(causally) impossible" and "(causally) necessary"?

An intuitive criterion of lawlikeness proposed by both Nelson Goodman and Roderick Chisholm [3] is that a lawlike generalization supports counterfactual inferences. Suppose I come upon a fruit

[1] For an explanation of the problem of counterfactual conditionals, and its relation to the problem of scientific laws, see *Introduction*, Sec. IX.—Ed.

[2] "Material implication" refers to the use of "if-then" in modern logic, as explained in *Introduction*, Sec. IV. "Analytic implication" refers to implications which hold as a matter of definition.—Ed.

[3] N. Goodman, "The Problem of Counterfactual Conditionals," reprinted in L. Linsky, ed., *Semantics and the Philosophy of Language* (Urbana, Ill.: Uni-

that looks like an orange but then turns out to taste like tangerines. If my friend insisted that, just the same, it is an orange, it would be quite proper for me to exclaim, "But if it were an orange, it would taste like an orange!" We do not, in such a case, admit that the generalization "All oranges taste like oranges" has been refuted, for we have such confidence in it that we refuse application of the term "orange" to a thing that does not taste like an orange. This does not mean that the generalization is merely analytic of the meaning of "orange," as long as we can conceive of circumstances under which we would admit that a thing that does not taste like most things that are normally called oranges still *is* an orange. Suppose the thing before us not only satisfies the visual and tactual tests of orangehood but also grew on an orange tree and has just the same anatomy as fruits growing on orange trees; in that case one may be strongly inclined to admit that there are "freak" oranges that do not taste like "normal" oranges.

Similarly, if a physicist came upon an apparently freely falling body whose acceleration fluctuated considerably, he would say, "This body cannot be falling freely; if it were falling under the sole influence of gravity, it would fall with constant acceleration; there must be some disturbing force that is responsible for this deviation from the norm." Again, this does not mean that he treats the law of freely falling bodies as an irrefutable analytic statement, as a definition of "freely falling body." As a responsible scientist, he would search for disturbing forces; that failing, he might examine the body to see whether in some conceivably relevant respects it differed from the bodies whose gravitational behavior was normal, and whatever the outcome of this examination might be he would either have to abandon the law of freely falling bodies in its present form or else would have to abandon some other physical principles that are logically involved. If the abnormally behaving body had, say, a chemical property P, and other bodies with P were found to fall similarly, he might restrict the law to "All freely falling bodies fall with constant acceleration unless they have P," even though this course would compel him to abandon the very important principle that the effect of gravity on a given body does not depend on any intrinsic properties (but only on the location) of that body.

versity of Illinois Press, 1952) and in N. Goodman, *Fact, Fiction, and Forecast* (Cambridge: Harvard University Press, 1955), chap. 1; R. Chisholm, "The Contrary-to-Fact Conditional," reprinted in H. Feigl and W. Sellars, *Readings in Philosophical Analysis* (New York: Appleton-Century-Crofts, Inc., 1949).

And if no relevant difference were discovered, the law could not even partially be saved by restricting its scope, unless one or the other of the following assumptions were given up instead: (1) That the clocks employed in measuring the time lapses corresponding to the successive positions were accurate. He might assume that unknown forces disturbed, not the falling body, but the clock (even though the postulate of causality would not allow him to rest satisfied with such an ad hoc assumption until the postulated "disturbers" were actually tracked down). (2) That the measuring rods employed in measuring the displacements were not rigid but contracted and expanded—again by forces unknown for the time being —so as to produce the appearance of fluctuating acceleration. The point is that unlike a simple analytic statement ("All freely falling bodies fall under the sole influence of gravity," for example) a physical law can be maintained under the pressure of apparently disconfirming evidence *only* by abandoning other factual assumptions that are logically involved in the process of testing it.

By contrast, if on examining the contents of my purse I announce, "All the coins in my purse are nickels," this statement, though universal in form, cannot support a counterfactual such as "If that coin—it looks like a dime from where I stand—were in my purse, it would be a nickel." It would be more natural to infer the counterfactual "If that coin were in my purse, then not all the coins in my purse would be nickels." Similarly, though it may be true that all the people who ever sat on a certain park bench as long as the park bench existed were redheads, this true universal statement could hardly support the counterfactual "If Cary Grant had been sitting on that park bench, he would have been a redhead"; the proper inference is rather "If Cary Grant had been sitting on that park bench, then not all the people who sat on it would have been redheads."

Although this intuitive test of lawlikeness of a generalization, as contrasted with merely *accidental* universality, has some surface appeal as a criterion, it obviously will not do as an *analysis* of lawlikeness. For, as we have seen, we need to invoke the concept "lawlike generalization" in order to explain how a counterfactual conditional can be asserted with warrant; hence it would be running around in a circle to define a lawlike generalization as a universal statement that warrants a counterfactual conditional. But even its value as a criterion of distinction is open to doubt. According to deductive logic, the premises "All A are B" and "x is an A"

entail the conclusion "*x* is a *B*" in any case. Let us assume that the constants that may be substituted for *x* are just indexical signs, i.e., expressions that "point" or identify without characterizing the object, such as "that thing" or "the thing at place *P* at time *t*." Then the universal premise "All *A* are *B*," whether lawlike or not, entails any statement of the form "If *x* is an *A*, then *x* is a *B*." And if we assume that all *A* are *B*, we can justifiably assert "If *x* were an *A*, then necessarily *x* would be a *B*," the necessity being relative to that assumption.

Thus, if I have made quite certain that all the coins presently in my pocket are nickels, I am perfectly justified in asserting "If that object—whatever it may be—were a coin presently in my pocket, it would be a nickel," for the subjunctive mood here really expresses a logically necessary connection between "All the coins presently in my pocket are nickels" and "If that object is a coin presently in my pocket, then it is a nickel." To say "If that dime were in my pocket now, it would be a nickel" sounds paradoxical because in *characterizing* the object as a dime, I have already excluded its being a nickel, and then my statement suggests that by being transferred to my pocket the dime could be converted into a nickel. In inferring, on the contrary, ". . . , then not all the coins presently in my pocket would be nickels," I drop the assumption that all the coins presently in my pocket are nickels and perform the necessary deduction of the proposition "Some of the coins presently in my pocket are not nickels" from the supposed proposition "That dime is presently in my pocket." But surely there would be just the same justification for the counterfactual "If that dog were a raven, then some ravens would not be black," or "If the moon were a planet, then at least one planet would not revolve in an elliptical orbit around the sun." In each of these cases of inferring the negation of the universal statement "All *A* are *B*" from the counterfactual assumption the object of the counterfactual assumption is tacitly characterized by a property that is incompatible with *B*. And if this is permitted, the universal statement will, of course, be unable to support a counterfactual inference whether or not it be accidental. This holds as well for our example of Cary Grant and the redheads: if Cary Grant were just indexically identified, and all other knowledge about him —such as that he never sat on the park bench in question!—were suppressed, then one who had made sure that all the people who ever sat there were redheads would be perfectly justified in saying,

"Well, if this man were one of those who sat there, he would be a redhead." The statement can have a paradoxical ring only for one who knows that Cary Grant's hair is not red and hence is puzzled by the suggestion of a causal connection between a man's hair color and his sitting accidentally on some park bench.

B. THE CRITERION OF UNRESTRICTED GENERALITY

Those who believe that empirical science can be adequately expressed in a language having the structure of *Principia Mathematica*, i.e., an object-language devoid of such modal expressions as "necessarily" and "possibly" (though the notion of logical consequence can be formulated in the metalanguage), face a trying test of their faith. They must, of course, admit that lawlike generalizations cannot be simply equated with synthetic formal implications, nor can they invoke the criterion just criticized. Some have proposed *unrestricted generality* as the mark of lawlikeness, in a sense to be explained forthwith.

Some universal statements seem to refer essentially to a particular object or to a particular place or to a particular time. Thus the examples discussed in the preceding section refer to a particular trouser pocket, a particular time, a particular park bench. Let us call expressions by which we designate particular objects, times, or places *individual constants,* and predicates by means of which we talk about repeatable qualities or relations and that are not defined in terms of individual constants *purely general* (for convenience, we shall extend this term also to physical functors). And an individual constant will be said to occur essentially in a statement p if it occurs in p and p is not translatable without change of meaning into a statement in which it does not occur. As a first approximation one might then define a lawlike generalization as a synthetic universal statement in which no individual constants occur essentially. It is true that with some luck we might always succeed in eliminating individual constants from the formulation of a mere coincidence because we might find that the particular in question could be *uniquely described* by means of purely general predicates. Thus, if it so happened that the park bench mentioned in our example was the only park bench ever sat upon by a toothless drunkard, we could formulate the following true formal implication: For any x, if there is a time at which x sits on a park bench on which a toothless drunkard sits at some time, then x is a redhead.[4] Nevertheless, it would not follow that the individual constant "that park bench" occurred inessentially in the original statement, for the supposition on the basis of which the individual constant was eliminated is factual, not analytic. If it is true, the purely general statement will have the same truth-value as the original statement, but not the same meaning.

On the other hand, there are many statements containing individual constants essentially that we would want to characterize as lawlike: (1) "All the ice cubes now in this refrigerator will turn into water when heated," (2) "All the planets continually revolve around the sun in elliptical orbits," (3) "All freely falling bodies near the earth fall with a constant acceleration of 32 ft/sec^2," (4) "All freely falling bodies near the earth fall with the same acceleration, regardless of differences of mass." In the case of (1) and (4), a deduction from universal statements that contain no individual constants at all is feasible, and this has suggested to some the definition of a *fundamental* lawlike statement as a synthetic universal statement in which no individual constants occur essentially, and of a *derivative* lawlike statement as one that is deducible from a fundamental lawlike statement though it contains individual constants essentially. The so-called laws of motion and the law of universal gravitation, from which (4) is easily deducible, are obvious examples of fundamental lawlike statements in the defined sense: they do not mention any particular body nor any particular time or place. Yet, unfortunately, (2) and (3) are not lawlike at all according to this criterion. Kepler's first law of planetary motion follows from the axioms of Newtonian mechanics only on the assumption that the motion of a given planet is determined by solar attraction alone, but this assumption can be justified only by information concerning the relative masses of the bodies in the solar system: it is because the masses of the other planets are small in comparison with the mass of the sun that the gravitational attractions they exert are negligible and the problem of planetary revolution can be treated as a so-called "two-body problem." Without singular premises about the bodies in the solar system, therefore, (2) is not deducible from the general axioms of Newtonian mechanics. Similarly, in order to establish (3) deductively within the Newtonian theory, we have to know the earth's radius and mass.

---

[4] "Sits" is here meant as the tenseless form of "to sit," not as the present tense.

A further difficulty facing this approach is that it is not entirely clear that the predicates and functors in the postulates of an empirically interpreted theory are purely general. Length is operationally defined in terms of the standard meter, weight in terms of the standard gram. These units of measurement can, of course, be indefinitely duplicated once an appropriate relation of equality has been defined, but unless some *particular* body were designated as "the" standard meter or "the" standard gram, measurement could not begin at all. One may perhaps reply that though a particular body must be conventionally chosen as the standard body, the scientist can choose between it and any other body that is in the relevant respect equal to it. Just so we can defend the claim that "red" is a purely general predicate though it must be ostensively defined in terms of some red particular or other, because it is not necessary that one refer to *this* rather than *that* red particular. But this line of defense would seem to break down for a very fundamental concept of mechanics: the concept of an inertial system. It is, of course, involved in the law of inertia: any isolated body is at rest or in uniform motion relative to any inertial system. It is also involved in the postulate of the special theory of relativity that the velocity of light (*in vacuo*) is the same in all inertial systems. What is meant by an inertial system? Three definitions may be considered:

1. A system relative to which an isolated body is either at rest or in uniform motion. The obvious objection to (1) is that it turns the law of inertia into an innocuous tautology, whereas it has in fact a significant predictive and explanatory use. It is used, for example, jointly with the law of freely falling bodies and the law of independence of forces to derive the parabolic trajectory of a projectile.

2. A system in which no inertial forces, such as centrifugal forces, manifest themselves. But the test of inertial force is (*a*) a subjective one, pulls or pushes experienced by an observer, such as the centrifugal outward pull on a merry-go-round, or the forward pull experienced by the passengers when the bus suddenly slows down. If so, the defined concept of inertial system would be inapplicable to physical systems in outer space, but the laws of motion *are* used in astronomy. Or else (*b*) inertial forces are *definitionally* inferred when the observed accelerations cannot be fitted into the formula "$F = m \cdot a$" on the assumption that only what Newton called "impressed" forces are involved. Thus, if a ball were rolled on the floor of a moving train in the direction of motion and at that very moment the train came to a sudden stop, the resultant acceleration of the

ball would exceed the ratio of the force that was "impressed" on it to its mass; hence the action of an inertial force (due to an "absolute" acceleration of the train) could be inferred by just measuring the ball's total acceleration and noting that it exceeds the amount entailed by the second law of motion. Clearly, this definition of inertial force, and therewith inertial system, is again irreconcilable with the factual import of the laws of motion.

3. A system that is not accelerated relative to the fixed stars. This last definition is the one usually adopted by physicists, probably because it is "operational" and prevents the laws of motion from collapsing into idle tautologies. But since "the fixed stars" is an individual constant, "inertial system" is not, then, a purely general predicate, and the laws of motion, as well as the law of the constancy of the velocity of light in all inertial systems, would not be fundamental laws.

C. TEMPORAL INVARIABILITY

Some have contended that a law of nature is essentially a functional relation that remains constant in time. That nature is "uniform" means, on this view, just that there are relatively simple functional relations between physical variables that do not vary as time goes on. The type of law that has suggested this definition is, of course, a differential law of mathematical physics. Thus the law of gravitation expresses the acceleration of a gravitating body as a function of its distance from the attracting body: $d^2r/dt^2 = f(r)$. But it is not clear why the functional relations invariance in time should be deemed more "essential" than its invariance in space. When the law is fully stated, it says: For any body x that revolves around a central body of mass M under the sole influence of gravity emanating from that central body, no matter *where* in space the revolving motion occurs, and *for any time t*, if d^2r/dt^2 is the (gravitational) acceleration of x at t and r the simultaneous distance of x from the central body, then

$$d^2r/dt^2 = G \cdot M/r^2$$

In the terminology of symbolic logic, a universal quantifier binding a space-variable is just as essential for a complete statement of the law as a universal quantifier binding time-variable; otherwise one might ask, for example, whether this functional relation is meant to hold only for our solar system or for any region of space.

Again, it has been asserted that it is definitory of "law of nature" that the time-variable is not one of the arguments on which the function depends, that it does not occur "explicitly" in the equation though, of course, it may occur "implicitly" through the definitions of derivatives (such as acceleration). In our example, in order to calculate the planet's acceleration at a given moment the physicist must know the value of r at that moment but he need not know what time it is. But the time-variable does occur explicitly in the equations of motion that are derived from the differential equations by integration. Thus, consider the simplest case of a differential equation of classical dynamics, that describing a falling motion under a constant force:

$$\frac{d^2z}{dt^2} = g$$

Integration yields first:

$$\frac{dz}{dt} = g \cdot t + v_1$$

where v_1 is the velocity at an initial instant t_1—which may or may not be zero, and t is the time lapse; and next:

$$z = \tfrac{1}{2}g \cdot t^2 + v_1 t + z_1$$

(If z_1, the initial position, is taken as zero, and the body falls from rest, this equation reduces to $z = \tfrac{1}{2}g \cdot t^2$, Galileo's law, where g represents a constant to be determined by measurement.) And it seems somewhat arbitrary to withhold the title "law of nature" from integrated equations of motion and to restrict it to differential equations of motion.

A more acceptable criterion recognizing that space and time are on a par as regards the postulated uniformity of laws of nature is Maxwell's criterion: neither space-coordinates nor time-coordinates should occur "explicitly" in equations expressing laws of nature. Obviously "coordinates" here must mean particular values of the variables x, y, z, t, not the variables themselves. So understood, Maxwell's criterion is simply the criterion of unrestricted generality applied to the functional laws of physics: if no individual constants are to occur essentially in a lawlike statement, then coordinate descriptions of particular regions of space-time are excluded. From what has already been said in Section A it follows, however, that only what may be called *fundamental* laws satisfy this condition.

RUDOLF CARNAP

Probability and Inductive Logic

Rudolf Carnap, one of the leading figures of the Vienna Circle and of the "Logical Empiricist" movement, taught at the Universities of Vienna and Prague. In this country, he taught at the University of Chicago from 1936 to 1953; since leaving Chicago, he has been at the University of California at Los Angeles. Among his many influential books are: The Logical Syntax of Language; Introduction to Semantics; Foundations of Logic and Mathematics; Meaning and Necessity; *and* Logical Foundations of Probability, *from which the following material is extracted.*

[I. THE PROBLEM OF THIS BOOK]

The chief tasks of this book will be:

1) a clarification and, if possible, a definition of the concept of *degree of confirmation;*
2) a clarification of the logical nature of *induction* and, if possible, a construction of a system of *inductive logic;*
3) a clarification of the concept of *probability.*

At the present only a few preliminary explanations of these problems will be given.

1. When scientists speak about a scientific law or a theory, or also a singular statement, for example, a prediction, on the one hand, and certain observational data or experimental results, on the other, they often state a relation between those items in forms like these:

a. 'This experiment again confirms the theory T' (or: '. . . supplies new evidence for . . .').

b. 'The quantum theory is confirmed to a considerably higher degree by the experimental data known today than by those available twenty years ago' (or: '. . . is supported more strongly by . . .').

The concepts of confirming evidence or degree of confirmation used in statements of this kind are usually sufficiently well understood for simple, practical purposes, but they are hardly ever precisely explained. It will be one of the chief tasks of this book to

From Rudolf Carnap, *Logical Foundations of Probability* (Chicago: Univ. of Chicago Press, 1950), pp. 1–3, 20–27, 163, 207–208, 221–226. Copyright 1950 by The University of Chicago.

make concepts of this kind precise and to furnish a theory of the logical relations between any hypothesis and any piece of knowledge that might be regarded as confirming evidence for the hypothesis.

2. The problem of induction in the widest sense—concerning a hypothesis of any, not necessarily universal form—is essentially the same as the problem of the logical relation between a hypothesis and some confirming evidence for it. Thus, by laying down a definition for the concept of degree of confirmation and constructing a logical theory based upon this concept, we shall furnish a system of inductive logic. While deductive logic may be regarded as the theory based upon the concept of logical consequence or deducibility, inductive logic is the theory based upon what might be called the degree of inducibility, that is, the degree of confirmation.

3. The problem of probability is likewise closely related to that of induction. This has often been observed, at least with respect to one of the various conceptions of probability which we find in the historical development (sometimes called inductive probability). We shall try to show that we have to distinguish chiefly two concepts of probability; the one is defined in terms of frequency and is applied empirically, the other is a logical concept and is the same as degree of confirmation. It will be shown that both are important for the method of science, and thus the controversy between the two "conceptions" of probability will be dissolved.

Thus we see that one or several of the problems which we intend to approach have the following character. There is a certain term ('confirming evidence', 'degree of confirmation', 'probability') which is used in everyday language and by scientists without being exactly defined, and we try to make the use of these terms more precise or, as we shall say, to give an *explication* for them. . . .

The task of *explication* consists in transforming a given more or less inexact concept into an exact one or, rather, in replacing the first by the second. We call the given concept (or the term used for it) the *explicandum,* and the exact concept proposed to take the place of the first (or the term proposed for it) the *explicatum.* The explicandum may belong to everyday language or to a previous stage in the development of scientific language. The explicatum must be given by explicit rules for its use, for example, by a definition which incorporates it into a well-constructed system of scientific either logicomathematical or empirical concepts. . . .

[II. CONFIRMATION, PROBABILITY, AND INDUCTION]

The procedure of confirmation is a complex procedure consisting of components of different kinds. In this book we are concerned only with what may be called the logical aspect of confirmation, namely, with certain logical relations between sentences (or propositions expressed by these sentences). Within the practice of the procedure of confirmation, these relations are of interest to the scientist, for instance, in the following situation. He intends to examine a certain hypothesis h; he makes many observations of particular events which he regards as relevant for judging the hypothesis h; he formulates the results of all observations made or as much of them as are relevant in a report e, which is a long sentence. Then he tries to determine whether and to what degree the hypothesis h is confirmed by the observational evidence e. This last question alone is what we shall be concerned with. We call it a logical question because, once a hypothesis is formulated by h and any possible evidence by e (it need not be the evidence actually observed), the problem whether and how much h is confirmed by e is to be answered merely by a logical analysis of h and e and their relations. This question is not a question of facts in the sense that factual knowledge is required to find the answer. The sentences h and e, which are studied, do themselves certainly refer to facts. But, once h and e are given, the question mentioned requires only that we be able to understand them, that is, to grasp their meanings, and to establish certain relations which are based upon their meanings. Since we take semantics as the theory of the meanings of expressions in language and especially of sentences (this will be explained later), the relations between h and e to be studied may be characterized as semantical; therefore we call them *semantical concepts of confirmation*.

The question of confirmation in which we are here interested has been characterized above as a logical question. In order to avoid misunderstandings, a qualification should here be made. The question mentioned does not belong to deductive logic but to inductive logic. . . . Both branches have in common that the solution of their problems does not require factual knowledge but only analysis of meaning; therefore both parts of logic belong to semantics. This similarity makes it possible to explain the logical character of the relations of confirmation by an analogy with a more familiar relation in deductive logic, viz., the relation of *h* being a logical consequence of *e*, in our terminology, the relation of L-implication (i.e., logical implication or entailment, in distinction to material implication) between *e* and *h*. Let *e* be the sentence 'all men are mortal, and Socrates is a man', and *h* the sentence 'Socrates is mortal'. Both *e* and *h* have factual content. But, in order to answer the question whether *e* L-implies *h*, we need no factual knowledge, we need not know whether *e* is true or false, whether *h* is true or false, whether anybody believes in *e* and, if so, on what basis. All that is required is a logical analysis of the meanings of the two sentences. Analogously, to answer the question how much a hypothesis *h* is confirmed by an observational report *e*—a question in logic, but here in inductive, not in deductive, logic—we need not know whether *e* is true or false, whether *h* is true or false, whether anybody believes in *e* and, if so, on the basis of observations or just by imagination or in whatever way else. All we need is a logical analysis of the meanings of the two sentences. That is the reason why we call our problem the logical or semantical problem of confirmation, in distinction to what might be called methodological problems of confirmation, e.g., how best to construct an apparatus and to arrange it for certain experiments, how to carry out the experiments, how to observe the results, etc., all this for the purpose of an experimental examination of a given hypothesis.

In this book we shall deal with *three semantical concepts of confirmation*. Although in the application outlined above, the evidence is usually an observational report and the hypothesis a law or a prediction, we shall not restrict our concepts of confirmation to any particular contents or forms of the two sentences. . . .

(i) *The classificatory concept of confirmation* is that relation between two sentences *h* and *e* which is usually expressed by sentences of the following forms:

'*h* is confirmed by *e*.'
'*h* is supported by *e*.'
'*e* gives some (positive) evidence for *h*.'
'*e* is evidence substantiating (or corroborating) the assumption of *h*.'

Here *e* is ordinarily, as in the previous example, an observational report, but it may also refer to particular states of affairs not yet known but merely assumed and may even include assumed laws; *h* is usually a statement about an unknown state of affairs, e.g., a prediction, or it may be a law or any other hypothesis. It is clear that this concept of confirmation is a relation between two sentences, not a property of one of them. . . . Customary formulations which mention only the hypothesis are obviously elliptical; the evidence is tacitly understood. For instance, when a physicist says, 'This hypothesis is well confirmed,' he means '. . . on the evidence of the observational results known today to physicists.' . . .

(ii) *The comparative concept of confirmation* is usually expressed in sentences of the following or similar forms:

    a. '*h* is more strongly confirmed (or supported, substantiated, corroborated, etc.) by *e* than *h′* by *e″*.

Here we have a tetradic relation between four sentences. It may also be regarded as a dyadic relation between two pairs of sentences, *h,e* and *h′,e′*. In general, the two hypotheses *h* and *h′* are different from one another, and likewise the two bodies of evidence *e* and *e′*. Some scientists will perhaps doubt whether a comparison of this most general form is possible and may, perhaps, restrict the application of the comparative concept to those situations where two bodies of evidence are compared with respect to the same hypothesis (example (b)), or where two hypotheses are examined with respect to one evidence (example (c)). In either case the comparative concept is a triadic relation between three sentences.

    b. 'The general theory of relativity is more strongly confirmed by the results of laboratory experiments and astronomical observations known today than by those known in 1905.'

    c. 'The optical phenomena available to physicists in the nineteenth century were more adequately explained by the wave theory of light than by the corpuscular theory; in other words, they gave stronger support to the former theory than to the latter.' . . .

(iii) *The quantitative* (*or metrical*) *concept of confirmation,* the concept of *degree of confirmation.* Opinion seems divided as to whether or not a concept of this kind ever occurs in the customary talk of scientists, that is to say, whether they ever assign a numerical value to the degree to which a hypothesis is supported by given observational material or whether they use only classificatory and comparative concepts of confirmation. For the present discussion we leave this question open; even if the latter were the case, an attempt to find a quantitative explicatum for the comparative explicandum would be worth while. . . . In our general discussion of possible solutions the symbol '*c*' will be used for the degree of confirmation. Thus '$c(h,e) = q$' will be written for 'the degree of confirmation of *h* with respect to *e* is *q*'; here, *h* and *e* are sentences and *q* is a real number of the interval 0–1. . . .

The history of the theory of probability is the history of attempts to find an explication for the prescientific concept of probability. The number of solutions which have been proposed for this problem in the course of its historical development is rather large. The differences, though sometimes slight, are in many cases considerable. . . .

At the present we shall not enter a discussion of these various conceptions. While the main point of interest both for the authors and for the readers of the various theories of probability is normally the solutions proposed in those theories, we shall inspect the theories from a different point of view. We shall not ask what solutions the authors offer but rather which problems the solutions are intended to solve; in other words, we shall not ask what explicata are proposed but rather which concepts are taken as explicanda.

This question may appear superfluous, and the fact obvious, that the explicandum for every theory of probability is the prescientific concept of probability, i.e., the meaning in which the word 'probability' is used in the prescientific language. Is the assumption correct, however, that there is only one meaning connected with the word 'probability' in its customary use or, at the least, that only one meaning has been chosen by the authors as their explicandum? When we look at the formulations which the authors themselves offer in order to make clear which meanings of 'probability' they intend to take as their explicanda, we find phrases as different as 'degree of belief', 'credibility', 'degree of reasonable expectation', 'degree of possibility', 'degree of proximity to certainty', 'degree of partial truth', 'relative frequency', and many others. This multiplicity of phrases shows that any assumption of a unique explicandum common to all authors is untenable. We might even be tempted to go to the opposite extreme and to conclude that the authors are dealing not with one but with a dozen or more different concepts. However, I believe that this multiplicity is misleading. It seems to me that the number of explicanda in all the various theories of probability is neither just one nor about a dozen, but in all essential respects—leaving aside slight variations—very few and chiefly two. In the following discussions we shall use subscripts in order to distinguish these two principal meanings of the term 'probability' from which most of the various theories of probability start; we are, of course, distinguishing between two explicanda and not between the various explicata offered by these theories, whose number is much greater. The two concepts are (i) *probability*$_1$ = degree of confirmation; (ii) *probability*$_2$ = relative frequency in the long run. Strictly speaking, there are two groups of concepts, since, both for (i) and for (ii), there is a classificatory, a comparative, and a quantitative concept; however, at the present moment, we may leave aside these distinctions.

. . . The chief topic of this book is the problem of an explication of probability$_1$.

. . . A theory of the concept of degree of confirmation, founded upon an explicit definition of this concept, would constitute a *quantitative inductive logic*. If a satisfactory quantitative explicatum is not found or—as some authors believe—can never be found, then we should have the more modest task of defining a comparative explicatum. This would lead to a *comparative inductive logic*. . . .

Probability$_1$, the logical concept of probability as explicandum, has been explained in the preceding section and will later be analyzed in greater detail. A few explanations may here be given for *probability*$_2$, just to make clear its distinction from probability$_1$. The theory of probability$_2$ itself lies outside the program of this book, which deals with inductive logic and therefore with probability$_1$. A typical example of the use of the term 'probability' in the sense of probability$_2$ is the following statement:

'The probability of casting an ace with this die is 1/6.'

Statements of this form refer to two properties (or classes) of events: (i) the reference class K, here the class of the throws of this die; and (ii) the specific property M, here the property of being a throw with any die resulting in an ace. The statement says that the probability$_2$ of M with respect to K is 1/6. The statement is tested by statistical investigations. A sufficiently long series of, say, n throws of the die in question is made, and the number m of these throws which yield an ace is counted. If the relative frequency m/n of aces in this series is sufficiently close to 1/6, the statement is regarded as confirmed. Thus, the other way round, the statement is understood as predicting that the relative frequency of aces thrown with this die in a sufficiently long series will be about 1/6. This formulation is admittedly inexact; but it is only intended to indicate the meaning of 'probability$_2$' as an explicandum. To make this concept exact is the task of the explication. . . .

We shall now briefly characterize some of the most important kinds of inductive inference; they are neither exhaustive nor mutually exclusive.

1. The *direct inference*, that is, the inference from the population to a sample. (It might also be called internal inference or downward inference.) *e* may state the frequency of a property *M* in the population, and *h* the same in a sample of the population.

2. The *predictive inference*, that is, the inference from one sample to another sample not overlapping with the first. (It might also be called external inference.) This is the most important and fundamental inductive inference. . . . The special case where the second sample consists of only one individual is called the *singular predictive inference.* . . .

3. The *inference by analogy*, the inference from one individual to another on the basis of their known similarity.

4. The *inverse inference*, the inference from a sample to the population. (It might also be called upward inference.) This inference is of greater importance in practical statistical work than the direct inference because we usually have statistical information only for some samples actually observed and counted and not for the whole population. Methods for the inverse inference (often called 'inverse probability') have been much discussed both in the classical period and in modern statistics. One of the chief stimulations for the developments of modern statistical methods came from the controversies concerning the validity of the classical methods for the inverse inference.

5. The *universal inference*, the inference from a sample to a hypothesis of universal form. This inference has often been regarded as the most important kind of inductive inference. The term 'induction' was in the past often restricted to universal induction. . . .

[III. ON THE POSSIBILITY OF A QUANTITATIVE INDUCTIVE LOGIC]

Quantitative inductive logic, when fully developed—as it has not been so far and will not be in this book—so as to be applicable to the whole language of physics, is intended to enable us to determine, for instance, which of two hypotheses in physics is more supported by the given set of observational results and hence, so to speak, inductively preferable. Those who are skeptical with respect to quantitative inductive logic point to the fact—and here they are certainly correct—that in the practice of science factors of very different kinds influence the choice of a hypothesis. Some seem to think that to determine this choice by a simple calculatory schema would be just as preposterous as to propose rules of calculation which are to determine for every man which of the available women is the best for him to marry.

In judging objections of the kind described, it is important to be clearly aware of what is and what is not the nature and task of inductive logic and especially of its distinction from the methodology of induction. Inductive logic alone does not and cannot determine the best hypothesis on a given evidence, if the best hypothesis means that which good scientists would prefer. This preference is determined by factors of many different kinds, among them logical, methodological, and purely subjective factors. . . .

. . . If a physicist deliberates whether or not to accept one hypothesis rather than another one on the basis of given observational results, then inductive logic can be of use to him only in one respect. It tells him whether one hypothesis is more supported than the other one; and, if the inductive logic applied is not only comparative but quantitative, it tells him to what degree the hypothesis considered is supported by the observations; this is, so to speak, the degree of partial entailment or partial logical implication. And he can obtain this help only if inductive logic is sufficiently developed and if he is able to find a way of applying it to his special case. All the other factors influencing his thinking and his decision are outside the scope of inductive logic. . . .

Even if we distinguish clearly the logical factors from the methodological and other nonlogical factors, the question of the possibility of a quantitative inductive logic is still far from being settled. There remain still two problems: (1) Can the logical factors be measured, that is, given numerical values? (2) Is it possible to find a mathematical function of these numerical values which would represent the degree of confirmation, that is, an adequate quantitative explicatum of probability$_1$? . . .

Some students regard as doubtful or impossible the numerical evaluation even of some of those factors which we characterize as logical. Let us examine, as examples, the factors mentioned in this connection by Kries. After discussing the inference by analogy . . . , he speaks about the universal inductive inference which leads from experience to laws, that is, sentences of a universal content. "Especially if a sentence of this kind", he says . . . , "possesses a great variety of consequences and is applicable in many cases and hence can be founded on experiential results of many different kinds, then it cannot be denied that a numerical measure of this foundation or empirical confirmation does not exist. To look for a numerical value of the certainty, for example, of the law of inertia or the principle of the conservation of energy would be an entirely illusory attempt; and the same holds for other, less well-established theorems of the same or other fields. For any sentence of this kind, extension and precision of its empirical confirmation, richness and fertility of its applications, and no less the objections against it which have to be eliminated by new assumptions, all these are factors which defy in principle any numerical determination." [1] By saying "in principle", Kries indicates that he intends to disregard the difficulties caused by the fact that the methods of inductive logic may not yet be sufficiently developed at the present moment and further by the fact that the immense complexity of the situation with respect to his examples may practically prevent us from carrying out the numerical evaluation. Of the factors he mentions, the following are of a logical nature, and a quantitative inductive logic is therefore required to take them into account for the calculation of the degree of confirmation: (i) the extension of the confirming observational material, (ii) the variety of the confirming material, (iii) the precision of the confirming material, (iv) the extension (and likewise the other factors just mentioned) of the disconfirming material. . . . In the passage quoted, Kries makes two different statements concerning these factors, constituting negative answers to the two questions earlier mentioned. He says (1) that "all these are factors which defy in principle any numerical determination" and (2) that therefore "a numerical measure of this . . . empirical confirmation does not exist". Now the great difficulty involved in (2) must be admitted; it will be discussed in greater detail in the next section. The assertion (1), however, seems rather surprising, because the

[1] J. von Kries, *Die Prinzipien der Wahrscheinlichkeitsrechnung*. Freiburg, 1886, pp. 29 f.

contrary appears nearly obvious and fairly generally assumed by scientists.

Let us subject this assertion to a closer examination. It says that it is impossible in principle to give numerical values to the factors mentioned—quite aside from the other question whether we can use these values for determining the degree of confirmation. There is first the problem of counting the number of confirming and of disconfirming cases for a given universal hypothesis h in a given observational report e. It is true, there are some serious difficulties involved in this problem, though often overlooked. It is usually assumed that, for all practical purposes, it is sufficiently clear what is meant by a confirming case and by a disconfirming case for h, and hence what is meant by the number of cases of those kinds occurring in e. The difficulties involved in these concepts were first pointed out by Carl G. Hempel in his investigations of the concept of confirmation. . . . Let us briefly indicate the chief difficulty. Let h be a simple law: '$(x)(Mx \supset M'x)$',[2] where 'M' and 'M''' are molecular predicates; h may say, for instance, that all swans are white. Let i be '$Mb \cdot M'b$' ('b is a white swan'). Then it seems natural to call b a confirming case for the law h. Let j be '$Mc \cdot \sim M'c$' ('c is a non-white swan'). Then it seems natural to call c a disconfirming case for h. Now, let i' be '$\sim Md \cdot \sim M'd$' ('d is a non-white non-swan'). At first, we might be tempted to regard d as an irrelevant case for h, that is, as neither confirming nor disconfirming. However, let h' be the law '$(x)(\sim M'x \supset \sim Mx)$' ('all non-white things are non-swans'); then i' has the same relation to h' as i to h, and hence d is a confirming case for h'. Now h and h' are L-equivalent; they express the same law and differ merely in their formulations. Therefore any observation must either confirm both or neither of them. On the other hand, if somebody who intends to test the law that all swans are white finds a non-swan, say, a stone, and observes that it is not white but brown, then he would probably hesitate to regard this observation as a confirming case for the law. We propose to call this puzzling situation *Hempel's paradox* because Hempel first pointed it out and offered a solution for it. . . . Hempel offers a definition for the concept of confirming case which is supposed to overcome this and other difficulties involved. Even

[2] In this formula, the symbol "(x)" is to be read, "No matter what x is . . .", or, more briefly, "For all x"; the formula as a whole, then, is read, "For all x, if x is M, then x is M'", or "All M is M'". The symbol "$\sim$" means "not."—Ed.

if there are some doubts whether the particular definition chosen by Hempel may not be too narrow, it seems plausible to assume that an adequate definition can be found. At any rate, nobody has so far given any reasons why it should be impossible in principle to find an adequate definition. On the contrary, scientists speak frequently about the number of confirming cases. A physicist would say, for instance, that he made six experiments in order to test a certain law and that he found it confirmed in all six cases. A physician would report that he tried out a new drug in twenty cases of a certain disease and found it successful in twelve cases, not successful in five, while in three cases the result was not clear either way; he hereby refers to confirming, disconfirming, and irrelevant cases for the hypothesis that the drug has a favorable effect in all cases of the disease in question. In other situations, the application of the concept of a confirming case would be less clear. This, however, shows merely that the concept is rather vague in certain respects; but all explicanda are more or less vague, and this fact certainly does not prove the impossibility of an explicatum.

Thus let us assume, as most scientists seem to do implicitly, that the concept of a confirming case can be defined; the concept of a disconfirming case is then easily definable. Then we can determine the number of confirming cases contained in the observational report e. If these cases are of different kinds, we can determine the number of confirming cases of each kind. Then it is not difficult to define a measure for the degree of variety in the distribution of the cases, on the basis of the number of kinds and the numbers of cases of each of the kinds. If the differences between the kinds are not only qualitative (for instance, male and female persons; or human beings, dogs, and guinea pigs) but quantitative (for instance, persons of different age, weight, blood pressure, etc.), then the degree of variety will also depend upon the dispersion of the cases with respect to each of the relevant magnitudes (measured, for instance, by the standard deviation). In this way we obtain numbers characterizing what Kries calls the extension and the variety of empirical confirmation. In the same way, the extension and the variety of the disconfirming material can be numerically determined.

That Kries should regard the precision with which the observations fulfill the law as a factor inaccessible to numerical evaluation is still more surprising. This factor comes into consideration only if the law contains quantitative concepts, for instance, physical magnitudes, and the report *e* refers to results of measurement of these magnitudes. Methods for measuring the precision in the sense here in question were developed a long time ago in the branch of mathematical statistics called the theory of errors and are constantly applied in many branches of science; for instance, a value inversely proportional to the standard deviation is often taken as a measure of precision. . . .

It is not quite clear what Kries means when he says that a law is "applicable in many cases" and refers to the "richness and fertility of its applications". Perhaps he means by "applications" of the law observable consequences; then the phrases just quoted do not refer to a new factor but are simply a repetition with other words of what he has said before. Or else he means by "applications" of the law its practically useful technological applications. In this case the factor referred to is not logical but methodological or technological. Hence, for the concept of degree of confirmation, it is neither required nor possible to take account of this factor.

Our discussion has shown that the first of the two arguments by which Kries and other authors try to prove the impossibility of a quantitative degree of confirmation is rather weak and can easily be refuted. The assertion is that certain logical factors, of which it is said correctly that the degree of confirmation depends upon them, are in principle inaccessible to numerical evaluation. We have seen that, on the contrary, it is rather plausible that they can be evaluated numerically.

After the elimination of the first of the two arguments by which Kries and other authors try to improve the impossibility of quantitative degree of confirmation, the second argument may be formulated like this: Even if it is true that numerical values can be attributed to each of the factors earlier mentioned, on which the degree of confirmation depends, it is still impossible to find a definition of a quantitative concept of degree of confirmation which adequately represents this dependence, because the parts played by the various factors differ from one another and vary with the situations and therefore cannot be summed up in one number.

Although this argument does not constitute a cogent proof of the impossibility asserted, the circumstances to which it refers deserve careful consideration, because they involve serious difficulties which any attempt toward a quantitative inductive logic has to meet.

[Carnap proceeds to discuss this second argument of Kries.—Ed.]

RICHARD RUDNER

An Introduction to Simplicity

*Richard Rudner received his B.A. from Queens College and his M.A.
and Ph.D. from the University of Pennsylvania. He has taught at Cornell, Tufts, Swarthmore, and Michigan State University, and at present
is Professor of Philosophy and Chairman of the Department, Washington University. He is editor-in-chief of the journal,* Philosophy of Science, *and is the author of a number of articles.*

Whatever may be the case for the serenity or unselfconsciousness
with which practicing scientists go about the business of accepting
or rejecting theories, it will surely not be denied that the problem
of constructing an adequate philosophical rationale for such practice remains in its perennial state of crisis. The recent past has witnessed monumental and illuminating attempts (such as those by
Reichenbach and Carnap) to provide that rationale essentially in
the form of a *logic of induction.* For the purposes of our present
concern it is not necessary to rehearse considerations of the cogency
of the objections that advocates of "objective" or "statistical" theories of induction have hurled against advocates of "logical theories
of confirmation" or, conversely, to consider the objections which
advocates of the latter view have hurled against those of the former.
It is not even necessary to go into the arguments which partizans
of *neither* of these points of view have leveled against both, nor
into those which partizans of either have leveled against such
"third" forces as recent theories of "Subjective" probability. The
unhappy fact is that in the matter of cogent objections against
theories of inductive inference, the recent philosophical literature
provides us with an embarrassment of riches.

The reason that none of these considerations need detain us for
the present, however, is to be found in the fact that even if any of
the types of programs for inductive logic mentioned above could be
brought to the successful consummation its proponents apparently
envisage, we would still not have been provided with a complete or

From Richard Rudner, "An Introduction to Simplicity," *Philosophy of Science,*
XXVIII, No. 2 (April 1961), pp. 109–115. Reprinted by permission of the
author, who is also editor of the journal.

general basis for choice among theories. There are weights other than that of evidential strength whose assessment is a necessary condition for rational (i.e. scientifically reliable) choice among hypotheses. One of these additional weights we may refer to as the *cost* associated with the acceptability of any hypothesis; and philosophers and many scientists (e.g., some who are concerned with Decision Theory) have in recent years come to give the explication of this notion something like the attention it has always warranted. Whatever the importance or the poignancy of the problems which attend the explication of cost, however, our concern here is not with it but with still a third weight whose explication is also a necessary condition for the achievement of an adequate theory of inductive inference: I refer, of course, to *simplicity*.

Now, allusions to simplicity in the literature of Science and of Philosophy are innumerable and immensely varied in intent and nuance; and before any fruitful consideration of the topic or its importance can be undertaken it is necessary to delimit to some extent the range of our attention. This can be accomplished by fitting, with a minimum of procrustean ferocity, all of the varied references to simplicity which we are heir to under a relatively uncomplicated classificational schema. Uses of 'simplicity' then, may be classified either as *Ontological* (i.e., extra-linguistic) or Descriptional (i.e., linguistic). Sub-classifications under these main rubrics are *Subjective* (i.e., psychological) and *Objective* (i.e., non-psychological). Moreover, under the rubric, *Descriptional,* it is also fruitful to distinguish *Notational* and *Logical* (or *Structural*) as further subclassifications. A few examples will be sufficient to provide the very rough degree of clarity which is all we presently require for these six category terms.

Consider, first, ontological simplicity. It is quite clear that a great many people who have employed 'simplicity' or its cognates have used the term to attribute certain characteristics to the Universe rather than to our descriptions of the Universe. For such individuals it has been the extra-linguistic universe, or some segment of it, which is said to exhibit or to fail to exhibit some degree or other of simplicity. Moreover, these attributions of ontological simplicity may be classed as *objective* or *subjective* in accordance with whether their import was that the universe is (or is not) simple *independently of how we perceive it* or whether the (extra-linguistic) universe is (or is not) perceived by us to be simple. If the intent of the usage is that 'simplicity' is a predicate of the universe independently of the perception of it, we shall classify that usage as *objective-ontological;* if 'simplicity' is taken as a predicate of our (extra-linguistic) responses to the (extra-linguistic) universe, we shall classify it as *subjective-ontological.* Attributions of simplicity both to the universe and our extra-linguistic responses to it, of course, abound in the literature of science and metaphysics. Such attributions have always seemed fundamentally obscure to me. Yet, having reminded ourselves of their occurrence, we need linger no longer over them than is required to note that it is not ontological simplicity but descriptional simplicity which is the focus of interest of theories of inductive inference. . . .

Turning from ontological to linguistic considerations, then, we may, under the category of *Descriptional Simplicity,* at once distinguish two kinds: *Notational* and *Logical.* Whether any general distinction between the Notational and the Logical simplicity of descriptions is ultimately tenable is, again, not in point here. In employing it, I wish merely to call attention to such differing properties of descriptions as, say, their *brevity* in contrast with the *degrees* of the predicates they contain. An attribution of simplicity to a description on the basis of such a notational property of it as the number of (e.g., alphabetical) characters it contains, independently of anyone's psychological responses to such a property, will be classed as an instance of Objective-Notational simplicity. On the other hand, an attribution of simplicity to a description on the basis of the familiarity of the notation, or its elegance, or its convenience, or its efficiency for manipulation, or any aesthetic quality it has, etc., will count as an instance of Subjective-Notational Simplicity.

In the sense just indicated, then, neither objective nor subjective notational simplicity is our topic of concern in what follows. What is being attended to is the logical (or, alternatively, the formal) simplicity of descriptions—and especially those descriptions which constitute scientific theories. Moreover, since our interest is not in how people psychologically respond to logical properties of theories, we may characterize our field of attention as Objective-Logical Simplicity. Hereafter in these comments references to simplicity, unless otherwise qualified, are intended as references to Objective-Logical Simplicity.

Realization of the importance of considerations of simplicity for the Philosophy of Science is a phenomenon of the relatively recent past. This is not altogether surprising in view of the fact that advances in Logic, upon application of which much of the significant work accomplished has depended, are themselves phenomena of this century. Despite the importance of achieving an adequate explication of the concept, sustained and significant work on its accomplishment has thus far been undertaken by only a relatively small circle of philosophers. In the quite recent past this circle has slowly widened as interest in the problem has come to be quickened or inspired under the impetus of the positive and detailed results achieved especially by Professor Goodman. In any case, however slowly launched, work by an increasing number of able men, is now under way and we can look forward with hopeful excitement to the solution of problems about simplicity which once appeared well nigh insuperable.

Perhaps the importance of attaining an adequate explication of simplicity can best be indicated by pointing out some aspects of its connection with systematism. . . .

System is no mere adornment of Science, it is its very heart. To say this is not merely to assert that it is not the business of Science to heap up unrelated, haphazard, disconnected bits of information, but to point out that it is an ideal of science to give an *organized* account of the universe—to connect, to fit together in logical relations the concepts and statements embodying whatever knowledge has been acquired. Such organization is, in fact, a necessary condition for the accomplishment of two of Science's chief functions: explanation and prediction.

The work that has been done, and the work currently being done so far as it is manifest, on objective-formal simplicity cannot plausibly be viewed to have brought us to a complete and adequate explication of the concept. It has, for its students, had the contrary effect of bringing a clearer realization of precisely how its problems ramify and of how much remains to be done. Nevertheless, if much remains to be done, what has already been done can fairly be said to have gotten the enterprise well under way and to give great promise of continued progress. And this *is* a towering accomplishment; for, hopelessness in the face of the problem of clarifying *simplicity* or (more or less disguised) flight from the problem have been the almost universal responses of the keenest intelligences which in the past have confronted it and its manifestations in the literature. Let us, even if briefly and too simply, review this accomplishment.

Each of two major avenues of approach, has been frequently referred to as a concern with formal simplicity. Yet, the two are fundamentally distinct and there is reason to regard with some misgiving (as I shall try to show below), this classification for one of the approaches. One of these lines of inquiry, the newer of them, has led toward an explication of the notion of the measurement of the formal simplicity of conceptual (i.e. predicate) bases of descriptional systems or theories. The considerable positive results which have been forthcoming are essentially the contribution of one man, Nelson Goodman; and they are, without doubt, results which fall under the category of objective-logical simplicity as it has been delineated above. The second line of inquiry, an older one, is associated with "the problem of curve fitting." The notion that in confrontation with data, representable as a set of graph points, the scientist should "induce to" the *simplest* ("smoothest") curve or function descriptive of that data, is of course, not unhackneyed. Such an admonition obviously raises the problem of how the *simplest* function among the alternatives available is to be discriminated. What would be cogent criteria of simplicity here? In light of what has been said above our interest will not be engaged by attempts to provide answers which are essentially ontological or subjective in character. In connection with criteria of objective simplicity, for the curve fitting problem over the past few decades, the work of three men, Harold Jeffreys, K. R. Popper, and John Kemeny, is especially noteworthy. Their problem is so often referred to as work on "the problem of *inductive* simplicity" that I shall for the present adopt this term though I believe it to be somewhat misleading. . . .

It might be thought that attempts such as Goodman's to clarify the notion of systemic simplicity would have an obvious focus on the simplicity properties of sets of postulates. Thus, a normal first impulse might be to say that of two otherwise equally adequate theories the one with the fewer postulates was objectively the simpler. But little reflection is needed to show both that this suggestion is unhelpful and also that its very lack of promise leads naturally to consideration of the simplicity of a theory's set of primitive predicates. For, the finite number of postulates of any theory can be trivially reduced to 1 by the simple operation of conjunction. By the criterion of number of postulates every theory would be equivalent to some theory which was maximally simple. Nor would it be possible to ameliorate this unwelcome result by any evident stipulation regarding the number of conjuncts in a set of postulates. For if the import of such a stipulation is, for example, that a postulate whose form is

$$(1)\ f_x \cdot g_x$$

is less simple than a postulate whose form is

$$(2)\ h_x$$

then the defectiveness of that stipulation becomes clear as soon as it is realized that it is always trivially possible to construct, i.e., to define or explicate a predicate, h, such that

$$(3)\ h_x \equiv (f_x \cdot g_x)$$

will be logically true. Accordingly, any postulate of finitely many conjuncts is trivially reducible to a postulate of one conjunct and by such a criterion all postulates must be regarded as equally simple. Even this unelaborate example indicates that to get at a relevant sense of 'simplicity' we must go beyond considerations of the number of, or gross logical structure of, postulates and come to grips with the logical structure of the *predicate* bases of theories.

Since it is plausible to assume that the theories we are interested in all share a common logical apparatus this means that attention turns to the formal simplicity of the extra-logical predicates. And this is, indeed, the route which Goodman follows. In the course of several years of work and through a process of increasingly successful modifications he has been able to construct a calculus of predicate simplicity which provides a measure of the simplicity of predicate bases of every relevant logical kind. In general, and necessarily vaguely, Goodman's assignments of simplicity values may be thought of as depending on the manner in which the extra-logical predicates of a theory *organize,* by virtue of such of their logical properties as reflexivity or symmetry, the entities comprising the total extension of the theory.

In coming to understand the import of Goodman's work it is especially important to avoid a confusion (not always avoided by earlier commentators on his work) between the simplicity of a basis and its *power.* The sets of predicates of two systems, S and S' are equally powerful if the sets are interdefinable. Suppose that no predicate of the set in S is defined by any other in S. If the *power* of a basis were the same thing as its simplicity, "no simpler basis for S . . . [could be arrived at than] . . . by taking all the predicates of S as primitive".[1] But, it is precisely the greater simplicity of an S' whose *primitive* basis is "narrower" (i.e., whose basis systematizes through defining the remainder of the predicates by a subset of the total number in the system), over an S whose basis is the "widest" possible which we desire to measure. In the last analysis what we are after is the *economy* of a system; and just as we get an indication of the economy of an automobile not from its having gone a certain distance but from how much gasoline it requires to go that distance, so too with the economy of systems. The *power* of a system is strictly analogous to the distance driven of our car in that knowing *it* alone will not give us a measure of economy. To arrive at the economy of a system we require also some measure of the simplicity of its basis—and it is this that Goodman's calculus attempts to provide.

[1] N. Goodman, "Recent Developments in the Theory of Simpicity," *Philosophy and Phenomenological Research*, **XIX** (1959), p. 430.

PART II

Historical Approaches

THOMAS KUHN

Paradigms and Some Misinterpretations of Science

Thomas Kuhn received his M.A. and Ph.D. in physics from Harvard; but while a graduate student, he began turning toward the history of science, and that study became his professional interest. Formerly professor of the history of science at the University of California, Berkeley, he is at present at Princeton. He is the author of The Copernican Revolution: Planetary Astronomy in the Development of Western Thought, *and of* The Structure of Scientific Revolutions.

. . . No process yet disclosed by the historical study of scientific development at all resembles the methodological stereotype of falsification by direct comparison with nature. That remark does not mean that scientists do not reject scientific theories, or that experience and experiment are not essential to the process in which they do so. But it does mean . . . that the act of judgment that leads scientists to reject a previously accepted theory is always based upon more than a comparison of that theory with the world. . . .

. . . There is no such thing as research without counterinstances. For what is it that differentiates normal science from science in a crisis state? Not, surely, that the former confronts no counterinstances. On the contrary, the puzzles that constitute normal science exist only because no paradigm that provides a basis for scientific research ever completely resolves all its problems. The very few that have ever seemed to do so (e.g., geometric optics) have shortly ceased to yield research problems at all and have instead become tools for engineering. Excepting those that are exclusively instrumental, every problem that normal science sees as a puzzle can be seen, from another viewpoint, as a counterinstance and thus as a source of crisis. . . .

. . . There are always some discrepancies. Even the most stubborn ones usually respond at last to normal practice. . . . during the sixty years after Newton's original computation, the predicted motion of the moon's perigee remained only half of that observed. As Europe's best mathematical physicists continued to wrestle unsuccessfully with the well-known discrepancy, there were occasional proposals for a modification of Newton's inverse square law. But no one took these proposals very seriously, and in practice this patience with a major anomaly proved justified. Clairaut in 1750 was able to show that only the mathematics of the application had been wrong and that Newtonian theory could stand as before. Even in cases where no mere mistake seems quite possible (perhaps because the mathematics involved is simpler or of a familiar and elsewhere successful sort), persistent and recognized anomaly does not always induce crisis. No one seriously questioned Newtonian theory because of the long-recognized discrepancies between predictions from that theory and both the speed of sound and the motion of Mercury. The first discrepancy was ultimately and quite unexpectedly resolved by experiments on heat undertaken for a very different purpose; the second vanished with the general theory of relativity after a crisis that it had had no role in creating. Apparently neither had seemed sufficiently fundamental to evoke the malaise that goes with crisis. They could be recognized as counterinstances and still be set aside for later work.

It follows that if an anomaly is to evoke crisis, it must usually be more than just an anomaly. . . . We therefore have to ask what it is that makes an anomaly seem worth concerted scutiny, and to that question there is probably no fully general answer. . . . Sometimes an anomaly will clearly call into question explicit and fundamental generalizations of the paradigm, as the problem of ether drag did for those who accepted Maxwell's theory. Or, as in the Copernican revolution, an anomaly without apparent fundamental import may evoke crisis if the applications that it inhibits have a particular practical importance, in this case for calendar design and astrology. . . . Presumably there are still other circumstances that can make an anomaly particularly pressing, and ordinarily several of these will combine. . . . one source of the crisis that confronted Copernicus was the mere length of time during which astronomers had wrestled unsuccessfully with the reduction of the residual discrepancies in Ptolemy's system.

When, for these reasons or others like them, an anomaly comes to seem more than just another puzzle of normal science, the transition to crisis and to extraordinary science has begun. The anomaly itself now comes to be more generally recognized as such by the profession. More and more attention is devoted to it by more and more of the field's most eminent men. If it still continues to resist, as it usually does not, many of them may come to view its resolution as *the* subject matter of their discipline. For them the field will no longer look quite the same as it had earlier. Part of its different appearance results simply from the new fixation point of scientific scrutiny. An even more important source of change is the divergent nature of the numerous partial solutions that concerted attention to the problem has made available. The early attacks upon the resistant problem will have followed the paradigm rules quite closely. But with continuing resistance, more and more of the attacks upon it will have involved some minor or not so minor articulation of the paradigm, no two of them quite alike, each partially successful, but none sufficiently so to be accepted as paradigm by the group. Through this proliferation of divergent articulations (more and more frequently they will come to be described as *ad hoc* adjustments), the rules of normal science become increasingly blurred. Though there still is a paradigm, few practitioners prove to be entirely agreed about what it is. Even formerly standard solutions of solved problems are called in question.

. . . All crises begin with the blurring of a paradigm and the consequent loosening of the rules for normal research. . . . And all crises close with the emergence of a new candidate for paradigm and with the subsequent battle over its acceptance. . . .

The transition from a paradigm in crisis to a new one from which a new tradition of normal science can emerge is far from a cumulative process, one achieved by an articulation or extension of the old paradigm. Rather it is a reconstruction of the field from new fundamentals, a reconstruction that changes some of the field's most elementary theoretical generalizations as well as many of its paradigm methods and applications. . . .

. . . Successive paradigms tell us different things about the population of the universe and about that population's behavior. They differ, that is, about such questions as the existence of subatomic particles, the materiality of light, and the conservation of heat or of energy. These are the substantive differences between successive paradigms, and they require no further illustration. But paradigms differ in more than substance, for they are directed not only to nature but also back upon the science that produced them. They are the source of the methods, problem-field, and standards of solution accepted by any mature scientific community at any given time. As a result, the reception of a new paradigm often necessitates a redefinition of the corresponding science. Some old problems may be relegated to another science or declared entirely "unscientific." Others that were previously non-existent or trivial may, with a new paradigm, become the very archetypes of significant scientific achievement. And as the problems change, so, often, does the standard that distinguishes a real scientific solution from a mere metaphysical speculation, word game, or mathematical play. The normal-scientific tradition that emerges from a scientific revolution is not only incompatible but often actually incommensurable with that which has gone before.

. . . Many readers will surely want to say that what changes with a paradigm is only the scientist's interpretation of observations that themselves are fixed once and for all by the nature of the environment and of the perceptual apparatus. On this view, Priestley and Lavoisier both saw oxygen, ·but they interpreted their observations differently; Aristotle and Galileo both saw pendulums, but they differed in their interpretations of what they both had seen.

. . . What occurs during a scientific revolution is not fully reducible to a reinterpretation of individual and stable data. . . . Rather than being an interpreter, the scientist who embraces a new paradigm is like the man wearing inverting lenses. Confronting the same constellation of objects as before and knowing that he does so, he nevertheless finds them transformed through and through in many of their details. . . .

The operations and measurements that a scientist undertakes in the laboratory are not "the given" of experience but rather "the collected with difficulty." They are not what the scientist sees—at least not before his research is well advanced and his attention focused. Rather, they are concrete indices to the content of more elementary perceptions, and as such they are selected for the close scrutiny of normal research only because they promise opportunity for the fruitful elaboration of an accepted paradigm. Far more clearly than the immediate experience from which they in part derive, operations and measurements are paradigm-determined. Science does not deal in all possible laboratory manipulations. Instead, it selects those relevant to the juxtaposition of a paradigm with the immediate experience that that paradigm has partially determined. As a result, scientists with different paradigms engage in different concrete laboratory manipulations. . . .

As for a pure observation-language, perhaps one will yet be devised. But . . . no current attempt to achieve that end has yet come close to a generally applicable language of pure percepts. And those attempts that come closest share one characteristic that strongly reinforces several of this essay's main theses. From the start they presuppose a paradigm. . . . Their result is a language that—like those employed in the sciences—embodies a host of expectations about nature and fails to function the moment these expectations are violated. . . . No language thus restricted to reporting a world fully known in advance can produce mere neutral and objective reports on "the given." Philosophical investigation has not yet provided even a hint of what a language able to do that would be like.

. . . As a result of the paradigm-embodied experience of the race, the culture, and, finally, the profession, the world of the scientist has come to be populated with planets and pendulums, condensers and compound ores, and other such bodies besides. Compared with these objects of perception, both meter stick readings and retinal imprints are elaborate constructs to which experience has direct access only when the scientist, for the special purposes of his research, arranges that one or the other should do so. . . . The scientist who looks at a swinging stone can have no experience that is in principle more elementary than seeing a pendulum. The alternative is not some hypothetical "fixed" vision, but vision through another paradigm, one which makes the swinging stone something else. . . .

It is . . . only after experience has been thus determined that the search for an operational definition or a pure observation-language can begin.

. . . From the beginning of the scientific enterprise, a textbook presentation implies, scientists have striven for the particular objectives that are embodied in today's paradigms. One by one, in a process often compared to the addition of bricks to a building, scientists have added another fact, concept, law, or theory to the body of information supplied in the contemporary science text.

But that is not the way a science develops. Many of the puzzles of contemporary normal science did not exist until after the most recent scientific revolution. Very few of them can be traced back to the historic beginning of the science within which they now occur. Earlier generations pursued their own problems with their own instruments and their own canons of solution. Nor is it just the problems that have changed. Rather the whole network of fact and theory that the textbook paradigm fits to nature has shifted. . . .

. . . Few philosophers of science still seek absolute criteria for the verification of scientific theories. Noting that no theory can ever be exposed to all possible relevant tests, they ask not whether a theory has been verified but rather about its probability in the light of the evidence that actually exists. And to answer that question one important school is driven to compare the ability of different theories to explain the evidence at hand. That insistence on comparing theories also characterizes the historical situation in which a new theory is accepted. Very probably it points one of the directions in which future discussions of verification should go.

In their most usual forms, however, probabilistic verification theories all have recourse to one or another of the pure or neutral observation-languages discussed. One probabilistic theory asks that we compare the given scientific theory with all others that might be imagined to fit the same collection of observed data. Another demands the construction in imagination of all the tests that the given scientific theory might conceivably be asked to pass. Apparently some such construction is necessary for the computation of specific probabilities, absolute or relative, and it is hard to see how such a construction can possibly be achieved. If, as I have already urged, there can be no scientifically or empirically neutral system of language or concepts, then the proposed construction of alternate tests and theories must proceed from within one or another paradigm-based tradition. Thus restricted it would have no access to all

possible experiences or to all possible theories. As a result, probabilistic theories disguise the verification situation as much as they
illuminate it. Though that situation does, as they insist, depend
upon the comparison of theories and of much widespread evidence,
the theories and observations at issue are always closely related to
ones already in existence. Verification is like natural selection: it
picks out the most viable among the actual alternatives in a particular historical situation. Whether that choice is the best that could
have been made if still other alternatives had been available or if
the data had been of another sort is not a question that can usefully
be asked. There are no tools to employ in seeking answers to it.

A very different approach to this whole network of problems has
been developed by Karl R. Popper who denies the existence of any
verification procedures at all.[1] Instead, he emphasizes the importance of falsification, i.e., of the test that, because its outcome is
negative, necessitates the rejection of an established theory. Clearly,
the role thus attributed to falsification is much like the one this
essay assigns to anomalous experiences, i.e., to experiences that, by
evoking crisis, prepare the way for a new theory. Nevertheless,
anomalous experiences may not be identified with falsifying ones.
Indeed, I doubt that the latter exist. As has repeatedly been empha-
sized before, no theory ever solves all the puzzles with which it is
confronted at a given time; nor are the solutions already achieved
often perfect. On the contrary, it is just the incompleteness and
imperfection of the existing data-theory fit that, at any time, define
many of the puzzles that characterize normal science. If any and
every failure to fit were ground for theory rejection, all theories
ought to be rejected at all times. On the other hand, if only severe
failure to fit justifies theory rejection, then the Popperians will require some criterion of "improbability" or of "degree of falsification."
In developing one they will almost certainly encounter the same
network of difficulties that has haunted the advocates of the various
probabilistic verification theories.

Many of the preceding difficulties can be avoided by recognizing
that both of these prevalent and opposed views about the underlying logic of scientific inquiry have tried to compress two largely
separate processes into one. Popper's anomalous experience is important to science because it evokes competitors for an existing

[1] K. R. Popper, *The Logic of Scientific Discovery* (New York, 1959), esp.
chaps. i-iv.

paradigm. But falsification, though it surely occurs, does not happen with, or simply because of, the emergence of an anomaly or falsifying instance. Instead, it is a subsequent and separate process that might equally well be called verification since it consists in the triumph of a new paradigm over the old one. Furthermore, it is in that joint verification-falsification process that the probabilist's comparison of theories plays a central role. Such a two-stage formulation has, I think, the virtue of great verisimilitude, and it may also enable us to begin explicating the role of agreement (or disagreement) between fact and theory in the verification process. To the historian, at least, it makes little sense to suggest that verification is establishing the agreement of fact with theory. All historically significant theories have agreed with the facts, but only more or less. There is no more precise answer to the question whether or how well an individual theory fits the facts. But questions much like that can be asked when theories are taken collectively or even in pairs. It makes a great deal of sense to ask which of two actual and competing theories fits the facts *better*. . . .

PIERRE DUHEM

Physical Theory, Mathematics, and Experiment

Pierre Duhem (1861–1916) was one of the leading French physicists of his day, contributing especially to the field of thermodynamics. He also was one of the founders of the modern subject of the history of science, with his monumental Léonard de Vinci *and* Le Système du Monde, *a history of cosmological speculation from Plato to Copernicus. His* The Aim and Structure of Physical Theory, *from which the following passages are taken, is one of the great classics in the philosophy of science, and anticipates many of the more recent discussions of a number of problems.*

[I. PHYSICAL THEORY]

Could we not assign an aim to physical theory that would render it *autonomous?* Based on principles which do not arise from any metaphysical doctrine, physical theory might be judged in its own terms without including the opinions of physicists who depend on the philosophical schools to which they may belong.

Could we not conceive a method which might be *sufficient* for the construction of a physical theory? Consistent with its own definition the theory would employ no principle and have no recourse to any procedure which it could not legitimately use.

We intend to concentrate on this aim and this method, and to study both.

Let us posit right now a definition of physical theory. . . . A physical theory is not an explanation. It is a system of mathematical propositions, deduced from a small number of principles, which aim to represent as simply, as completely, and as exactly as possible a set of experimental laws.

In order to start making this definition somewhat more precise, let us characterize the four successive operations through which a physical theory is formed:

From Pierre Duhem, *The Aim and Structure of Physical Theory*, trans. P. P. Wiener (Princeton: Princeton Univ. Press, 1954), pp. 19–21, 23–24, 132–135, 144–145, 147, 185–190, 211–212, *passim.* Used by permission of Princeton University Press.

1. Among the physical properties which we set ourselves to represent we select those we regard as simple properties, so that the others will supposedly be groupings or combinations of them. We make them correspond to a certain group of mathematical symbols, numbers, and magnitudes, through appropriate methods of measurement. These mathematical symbols have no connection of an intrinsic nature with the properties they represent; they bear to the latter only the relation of sign to thing signified. Through methods of measurement we can make each state of a physical property correspond to a value of the representative symbol, and vice versa.

2. We connect the different sorts of magnitudes, thus introduced, by means of a small number of propositions which will serve as principles in our deductions. These principles may be called "hypotheses" in the etymological sense of the word for they are truly the grounds on which the theory will be built; but they do not claim in any manner to state real relations among the real properties of bodies. These hypotheses may then be formulated in an arbitrary way. The only absolutely impassable barrier which limits this arbitrariness is logical contradiction either among the terms of the same hypothesis or among the various hypotheses of the same theory.

3. The diverse principles or hypotheses of a theory are combined together according to the rules of mathematical analysis. The requirements of algebraic logic are the only ones which the theorist has to satisfy in the course of this development. The magnitudes on which his calculations bear are not claimed to be physical realities, and the principles he employs in his deductions are not given as stating real relations among those realities; therefore it matters little whether the operations he performs do or do not correspond to real or conceivable physical transformations. All that one has the right to demand of him is that his syllogisms be valid and his calculations accurate.

4. The various consequences thus drawn from the hypotheses may be translated into as many judgments bearing on the physical properties of the bodies. The methods appropriate for defining and measuring these physical properties are like the vocabulary and key permitting one to make this translation. These judgments are compared with the experimental laws which the theory is intended to represent. If they agree with these laws to the degree of approximation corresponding to the measuring procedures employed, the

theory has attained its goal, and is said to be a good theory; if not, it is a bad theory, and it must be modified or rejected.

Thus a true theory is not a theory which gives an explanation of physical appearances in conformity with reality; it is a theory which represents in a satisfactory manner a group of experimental laws. A false theory is not an attempt at an explanation based on assumptions contrary to reality; it is a group of propositions which do not agree with the experimental laws. *Agreement with experiment is the sole criterion of truth for a physical theory. . . .*

Concerning the very nature of things, or the realities hidden under the phenomena we are studying, a theory conceived on the plan we have just drawn teaches us absolutely nothing, and does not claim to teach us anything. Of what use is it, then? What do physicists gain by replacing the laws which experimental method furnishes directly with a system of mathematical propositions representing those laws?

First of all, instead of a great number of laws offering themselves as independent of one another, each having to be learnt and remembered on its own account, physical theory substitutes a very small number of propositions, viz., fundamental hypotheses. The hypotheses once known, mathematical deduction permits us with complete confidence to call to mind all the physical laws without omission or repetition. Such condensing of a multitude of laws into a small number of principles affords enormous relief to the human mind, which might not be able without such an artifice to store up the new wealth it acquires daily. . . .

On the other hand, theory, by developing the numerous ramifications of the deductive reasoning which connects principles to experimental laws, establishes an order and a classification among these laws. It brings some laws together, closely arranged in the same group; it separates some of the others by placing them in two groups very far part. Theory gives, so to speak, the table of contents and the chapter headings under which the science to be studied will be methodically divided, and it indicates the laws which are to be arranged under each of these chapters. . . .

[II. MATHEMATICS IN PHYSICAL THEORY]

Mathematical deduction is an intermediary process; its object is to teach us that on the strength of the fundamental hypotheses of the theory the coming together of such and such circumstances will entail such and such consequences; if such and such facts are produced, another fact will be produced. For example, it will tell us that on the strength of the hypotheses of thermodynamics, when we submit a block of ice to a certain pressure, the block will melt when the thermometer reads a certain number.

Does mathematical deduction introduce directly into its calculations the facts we call circumstances in the concrete form in which we observe them? Does it draw from them the facts we call consequences in the concrete form in which we ascertain them? Certainly not. The apparatus used for compression, a block of ice, and a thermometer are things the physicist manipulates in the laboratory; they are not elements belonging to the domain of algebraic calculation. Hence, in order to enable the mathematician to introduce in his formulas the concrete circumstances of an experiment, it is necessary to translate these circumstances into numbers by the intermediary of measurements. For example, the words "a certain pressure" must be replaced by a certain number of atmospheres which he will substitute for the letter P in his equation. Similarly, what the mathematician will obtain at the end of his calculation is a certain number. It will be necessary to refer back to the method of measurement in order to make this number correspond to a concrete and observable fact; for example, in order to make the numerical value taken by the letter T in the algebraic equation correspond to a certain thermometer reading.

Thus at both its starting and terminal points, the mathematical development of a physical theory cannot be welded to observable facts except by a translation. In order to introduce the circumstances of an experiment into the calculations, we must make a version which replaces the language of concrete observation by the language of numbers; in order to verify the result that a theory predicts for that experiment, a translation exercise must transform a numerical value into a reading formulated in experimental language. As we have already indicated, the method of measurement is the dictionary which makes possible the rendering of these two translations in either direction.

But translation is treacherous: *traduttore, traditore* (to translate is to betray). There is never a complete equivalence between two texts when one is a translated version of the other. Between the concrete facts, as the physicist observes them, and the numerical symbols by which these facts are represented in the calculations of the theorist, there is an extremely great difference. . . .

First of all, let us consider what we shall call a *theoretical* fact, that is to say, that set of mathematical data through which a concrete fact is replaced in the reasoning and calculations of the theorist. For example, let us take this fact: The temperature is distributed in a certain manner over a certain body.

In such a theoretical fact there is nothing vague or indecisive. Everything is determined in a precise manner: the body studied is geometrically defined; its sides are true lines without thickness, its points true points without dimensions; the different lengths and angles determining its shape are exactly known; to each point of this body there is a corresponding temperature, and this temperature is for each point a number not to be confused with any other number.

Opposite this *theoretical* fact let us place the *practical* fact translated by it. Here we no longer see anything of the precision we have just ascertained. The body is no longer a geometrical solid; it is a concrete block. However sharp its edges, none is a geometrical intersection of two surfaces; instead, these edges are more or less rounded and dented spines. Its points are more or less worn down and blunt. The thermometer no longer gives us the temperature at each point but a sort of mean temperature relative to a certain volume whose very extent cannot be too exactly fixed. Besides, we cannot assert that this temperature is a certain number to the exclusion of any other number; we cannot declare, for example, that this temperature is strictly equal to 10°; we can only assert that the difference between this temperature and 10° does not exceed a certain fraction of a degree depending on the precision of our thermometric methods.

Thus, whereas the contours of the drawing are fixed by a line of precise hardness, the contours of the object are misty, fringed, and shadowy. It is impossible to describe the practical fact without attenuating by the use of the word "approximately" or "nearly" whatever is determined too well by each proposition; on the other hand, all the elements constituting the theoretical fact are defined with rigorous exactness.

Whence we have this consequence: An infinity of different theoretical facts may be taken for the translation of the same practical fact.

For example, . . . to say that the temperature of a body is 10°, or 9.99° or 10.01° is to formulate three incompatible theoretical facts, but these three incompatible facts correspond to one and the same practical fact when our thermometer is accurate only to a fifth of a degree.

A practical fact is not translated therefore by a single theoretical fact but by a kind of bundle including an infinity of different theoretical facts. Each of the mathematical elements brought together in order to constitute one of these facts may vary from one fact to another; but the variation to which it is susceptible cannot exceed a certain limit, namely, the limit of error within which the measurement of this element is blotted. The more perfect the methods of measurement are, the closer is the approximation and the narrower the limits but they never became so narrow that they vanish. . . .

[III.] PHYSICAL THEORY AND EXPERIMENT

. . . A law of physics is but the summary of an infinity of experiments that have been made or will be performable. Hence we are naturally led to raise the question: What exactly is an experiment in physics?

This question will undoubtedly astonish more than one reader. Is there any need to raise it, and is not the answer self-evident? What more does "doing an experiment in physics" mean to anybody than producing a physical phenomenon under conditions such that it may be observed exactly and minutely by means of appropriate instruments?

Go into this laboratory; draw near this table crowded with so much apparatus: an electric battery, copper wire wrapped in silk, vessels filled with mercury, coils, a small iron bar carrying a mirror. An observer plunges the metallic stem of a rod, mounted with rubber, into small holes; the iron oscillates and, by means of the mirror tied to it, sends a beam of light over to a celluloid ruler, and the observer follows the movement of the light beam on it. There, no doubt, you have an experiment; by means of the vibration of this spot of light, this physicist minutely observes the oscillations of the piece of iron. Ask him now what he is doing. Is he going to answer: "I am studying the oscillations of the piece of iron carrying this mirror?" No, he will tell you that he is measuring the electrical resistance of a coil. If you are astonished and ask him what meaning these words have, and what relation they have to the phenomena he has perceived and which you have at the same time perceived, he will reply that your question would require some very long explanations, and he will recommend that you take a course in electricity.

It is indeed the case that the experiment you have seen done, like any experiment in physics, involves two parts. In the first place, it consists in the observation of certain facts; in order to make this observation it suffices for you to be attentive and alert enough with your senses. It is not necessary to know physics; the director of the laboratory may be less skillful in this matter of observation than the assistant. In the second place, it consists in the interpretation of the observed facts; in order to make this interpretation it does not suffice to have an alert attention and practiced eye; it is necessary to know the accepted theories and to know how to apply them, in short, to be a physicist. Any man can, if he sees straight, follow the motions of a spot of light on a transparent ruler, and see if it goes to the right or to the left or stops at such and such a point; for that he does not have to be a great cleric. But if he does not know electrodynamics, he will not be able to finish the experiment, he will not be able to measure the resistance of the coil. . . .

An experiment in physics is the precise observation of phenomena accompanied by an *interpretation* of these phenomena; this interpretation substitutes for the concrete data really gathered by observation abstract and symbolic representations which correspond to them by virtue of the theories admitted by the observer. . . .

A physicist decides to demonstrate the inaccuracy of a proposition; in order to deduce from this proposition the prediction of a phenomenon and institute the experiment which is to show whether this phenomenon is or is not produced, in order to interpret the results of this experiment and establish that the predicted phenomenon is not produced, he does not confine himself to making use of the proposition in question; he makes use also of a whole group of theories accepted by him as beyond dispute. The prediction of the phenomenon, whose nonproduction is to cut off debate, does not derive from the proposition challenged if taken by itself, but from the proposition at issue joined to that whole group of theories; if the predicted phenomenon is not produced, not only is the proposition questioned at fault, but so is the whole theoretical scaffolding used by the physicist. The only thing the experiment teaches us is that among the propositions used to predict the phenomenon and to establish whether it would be produced, there is at least one error; but where this error lies is just what it does not tell us. The physicist may declare that this error is contained in exactly the proposition he wishes to refute, but is he sure it is not in another proposition? If he is, he accepts implicitly the accuracy of all the other propositions he has used, and the validity of his conclusion is as great as the validity of his confidence. . . .

We know that Newton conceived the emission theory for optical phenomena. The emission theory supposes light to be formed of extremely thin projectiles, thrown out with very great speed by the sun and other sources of light; these projectiles penetrate all transparent bodies; on account of the various parts of the media through which they move, they undergo attractions and repulsions; when the distance separating the acting particles is very small these actions are very powerful, and they vanish when the masses between which they act are appreciably far from each other. These essential hypotheses joined to several others, which we pass over without mention, lead to the formulation of a complete theory of reflection and refraction of light; in particular, they imply the following proposition: The index of refraction of light passing from one medium into another is equal to the velocity of the light projectile within the medium it penetrates, divided by the velocity of the same projectile in the medium it leaves behind.

This is the proposition that Arago chose in order to show that the theory of emission is in contradiction with the facts. From this proposition a second follows: Light travels faster in water than in air. Now Arago had indicated an appropriate procedure for comparing the velocity of light in air with the velocity of light in water; the procedure, it is true, was inapplicable, but Foucault modified the experiment in such a way that it could be carried out; he found that the light was propagated less rapidly in water than in air. We may conclude from this, with Foucault, that the system of emission is incompatible with the facts.

I say the *system* of emission and not the *hypothesis* of emission; in fact, what the experiment declares stained with error is the whole group of propositions accepted by Newton, and after him by Laplace and Biot, that is, the whole theory from which we deduce the relation between the index of refraction and the velocity of light in various media. But in condemning this system as a whole by declaring it stained with error, the experiment does not tell us where the error lies. Is it in the fundamental hypothesis that light consists in projectiles thrown out with great speed by luminous bodies? Is it in some other assumption concerning the actions experienced by light corpuscles due to the media through which they move? We know nothing about that. It would be rash to believe, as Arago seems to have thought, that Foucault's experiment condemns once and for all the very hypothesis of emission, i.e., the assimilation of a ray of light to a swarm of projectiles. If physicists had attached some value to this task, they would undoubtedly have succeeded in founding on this assumption a system of optics that would agree with Foucault's experiment.

In sum, the physicist can never subject an isolated hypothesis to experimental test, but only a whole group of hypotheses; when the experiment is in disagreement with his predictions, what he learns is that at least one of the hypotheses constituting this group is unacceptable and ought to be modified; but the experiment does not designate which one should be changed.

We have gone a long way from the conception of the experimental method arbitrarily held by persons unfamiliar with its actual functioning. People generally think that each one of the hypotheses employed in physics can be taken in isolation, checked by experiment, and then, when many varied tests have established its validity, given a definitive place in the system of physics. In reality, this is not the case. Physics is not a machine which lets itself be taken apart; we cannot try each piece in isolation and, in order to adjust it, wait until its solidity has been carefully checked. Physical science is a system that must be taken as a whole; it is an organism in which one part cannot be made to function except when the parts that are most remote from it are called into play, some more so than others, but all to some degree. If something goes wrong, if some discomfort is felt in the functioning of the organism, the physicist will have to ferret out through its effect on the entire system which organ needs to be remedied or modified without the possibility of isolating this organ and examining it apart.

. . . It is not between two hypotheses, the emission and wave hypotheses that Foucault's experiment judges trenchantly; it decides rather between two sets of theories each of which has to be taken as a whole, i.e., between two entire systems, Newton's optics and Huygens' optics.

But let us admit for a moment that in each of these systems everything is compelled to be necessary by strict logic, except a single hypothesis; consequently, let us admit that the facts, in condemning one of the two systems, condemn once and for all the single doubtful assumption it contains. Does it follow that we can find in the "crucial experiment" an irrefutable procedure for transforming one of the two hypotheses before us into a demonstrated truth? Between two contradictory theorems of geometry there is no room for a third judgment; if one is false, the other is necessarily true. Do two hypotheses in physics ever constitute such a strict dilemma? Shall we ever dare to assert that no other hypothesis is imaginable? Light may be a swarm of projectiles, or it may be a vibratory motion whose waves are propagated in a medium; is it forbidden to be anything else at all? Arago undoubtedly thought so when he formulated this incisive alternative: Does light move more quickly in water than in air? "Light is a body. If the contrary is the case, then light is a wave." But it would be difficult for us to take such a decisive stand; Maxwell, in fact, showed that we might just as well attribute light to a periodical electrical disturbance that is propagated within a dielectric medium.

Unlike the reduction to absurdity employed by geometers, experimental contradiction does not have the power to transform a physical hypothesis into an indisputable truth; in order to confer this power on it, it would be necessary to enumerate completely the various hypotheses which may cover a determinate group of phenomena; but the physicist is never sure he has exhausted all the imaginable assumptions. The truth of a physical theory is not decided by heads or tails.

. . . A disagreement between the concrete facts constituting an experiment and the symbolic representation which theory substitutes for this experiment proves that some part of this symbol is to be rejected. But which part? This the experiment does not tell us; it leaves to our sagacity the burden of guessing. Now among the theoretical elements entering into the composition of this symbol there is always a certain number which the physicists of a certain epoch agree in accepting without test and which they regard as beyond dispute. Hence, the physicist who wishes to modify this symbol will surely bring his modification to bear on elements other than those just mentioned.

But what impels the physicist to act thus is *not* logical necessity. It would be awkward and ill inspired for him to do otherwise, but it would not be doing something logically absurd; he would not for all that be walking in the footsteps of the mathematician mad enough to contradict his own definitions. More than this, perhaps some day by acting differently, by refusing to invoke causes of error and take recourse to corrections in order to reestablish agreement between the theoretical scheme and the fact, and by resolutely carrying out a reform among the propositions declared untouchable by common consent, he will accomplish the work of a genius who opens a new career for a theory.

Indeed, we must really guard ourselves against believing forever warranted those hypotheses which have become universally adopted conventions, and whose certainty seems to break through experimental contradiction by throwing the latter back on more doubtful assumptions. The history of physics shows us that very often the human mind has been led to overthrow such principles completely, though they have been regarded by common consent for centuries as inviolable axioms, and to rebuild its physical theories on new hypotheses.

M A R Y   H E S S E

The Role of Models in Scientific Theory

Mary Hesse received her Ph.D. from the University of London, and is now Lecturer in the Philosophy of Science at Cambridge University. Besides being the author of a number of articles, she has written two books, Forces and Fields, *which traces the history of the problem of action at a distance in physics, and* Models and Analogies in Science.

Because a model is drawn from a familiar and well-understood process, such as particle mechanics, it provides the context of natural expectations in terms of which a theory can be tested. If we now consider some of the mechanical models of nineteenth-century physics, not necessarily as literal descriptions of nature as in the naïve realist view, but as devices which were essential for rendering a theory intelligible and testable, it will be possible to describe their logical function more clearly than we have so far done. Such an account will then be found to throw light on the more complex problems connected with the use of models in modern physics.

The most obvious property of a satisfactory model is that it exhibits an analogy with the phenomena to be explained, that is, that there is some identity of structure between the model and the phenomena. Now one may say in a straightforward sense that there is an analogy between two branches of physics if the same mathematical structure appears in the theory of both, for example, the theories of heat and of electrostatics can be formulated in the same equations if one reads 'temperature' for 'potential', 'source of heat' for 'positive electric charge', and so on. When there is an analogy of this kind, one theory may be used as a model for the other, as Kelvin used the idea of heat flow, whose theory was already established, as a model for the field theory of electrostatics, which he was developing for the first time. In an extended sense, the word 'analogy'

From Mary B. Hesse, *Forces and Fields* (Edinburgh and London: Thomas Nelson & Sons Ltd), pp. 21–28. Used by permission of Nelson, and of Philosophical Library, New York.

may then be applied to the relation between the model itself, for example billiard-ball-like particles, and the entities which are postulated to account for the phenomena, for example gas molecules. To say that there is an analogy here is to assert correspondences between a variety of experimental measurements and certain numbers deduced from the theory of the model. For example if the appropriate calculations based on the theory of mechanics are made about the energy of colliding billiard-balls, we can obtain a series of numerical values which is the same as that given by a thermometer placed in a vessel containing the gas.

The reason why a model such as that implied in the dynamical theory of gases is not just a dispensable way of picturing the appropriate equations, is that the model can be generalised, extended and tested, and if necessary modified, as a purely formal deductive system cannot. The model can be tested, because it is a system of entities and processes whose behaviour is already known apart from the new experimental facts which it is being used to explain. The behaviour of a collection of particles moving at random in a closed vessel is described in the theory of dynamics independently of the experimental results about gases with which it is compared, and this means that further ramifications of the theory of colliding particles can be used to extend and test the theory of gases. Further questions can be asked, such as 'Are gas molecules like rigid balls or like elastic ones?', 'What is their diameter?', and so on, and the theory is tested and developed by devising experiments to answer questions like these suggested by the model.

In order to function in the way just described, models need not of course be mechanical. Mechanical models were on the whole preferred during the nineteenth century, but even in classical physics the model of gravitating particles was used for electricity and magnetism, electrical models for the theory of chemical combination, and the model of heat flow for field theory. What is required is not that the model be mechanical but that its properties be already known and described in terms of some, preferably mathematical, theory, and that it should have the 'open texture' which allows modifications and extensions to be made as may be appropriate for the explanation and prediction of new phenomena.

The difficulty that seems to arise in modern physics from this account of the indispensability of models is that no single model of classical type, using charged particles or waves, is adequate to explain the phenomena of the atomic domain, and it is sometimes said that in consequence we must not ask for picturable models, but must be content with formal mathematical hypotheses in which the paradoxes associated with particle and wave models do not arise. Now there are two things to be noticed at this point which indicate that it is misleading to draw such a conclusion. In the first place, physicists do in fact continue to use both particle and wave models, each in appropriate situations, even though they are at first sight mutually contradictory, and this is not only in condescension to readers of popular science, nor merely to assist in the teaching of students. It is an essential part of research in these fields, as a brief glance at original papers will show, and as the above arguments have indicated. But it is true that at a deeper level of theoretical investigation, where particle-like and wave-like behaviour both have to be taken into account, models of the classical type can be dropped, and the theory developed in apparently formal mathematical terms. What then becomes of our insistence that uninterpreted formal systems are not sufficient to provide theoretical explanation?

The difficulty is resolved when it is realised that mathematical theories are not necessarily (or perhaps ever) uninterpreted formalisms, if by that is meant mere collections of signs combined in arbitrary axioms and permitting inference according to arbitrary rules. It is difficult to show this in general terms, but perhaps it may be illustrated by some examples. When the physical model of wave-motion in a material medium had to be abandoned in physics, it left its traces in the kind of mathematics which was used, for this was still a mathematical language derived from the wave equations of fluid motion, and so, for the mathematician, it carried some of the imaginative associations of the original physical picture. Again, when Riemannian geometry is used in general relativity theory, it is not an uninterpreted formalism, but a natural extension of the two-dimensional geometry of the surface of a sphere, which is picturable, to the geometry of a three-dimensional space curved in a fourth dimension, which is not, but in which certain of the interpretations of the symbols such as 'geodesic' or 'radius of curvature' remain valid. Just as there may be many levels of interpretation of a set of dynamical equations from sentences involving colliding elastic balls to statements about pressure and volume of a gas, so there may be various interpretations of a theory of pure mathematics on different levels of abstractness, and involving more or less reference to the comparatively concrete statements of Euclidean geometry or of arithmetic. And these interpretations of an apparently formal mathematical scheme provide the open texture which enables the theory to be tested, generalised and modified, just as is the case with more concrete mechanical and electrical models. It therefore becomes appropriate to speak of 'mathematical models' alongside these more traditional types. It might be thought that the word 'model' is misleading here, since there is no concrete thing to be built or pictured, but the word is now sanctioned by widespread use in connection with sciences as diverse as cosmology and nuclear physics, brain physiology and Freudian psychology. In the case of fundamental physics at least what are called 'models' are now always partly or wholly mathematical in type, for example in cosmology, where 'world-models' are certainly not models in the picturable sense.

The question now arises as to how seriously these various kinds of model are to be taken. In showing that they are, after all, essential to theories, and not dispensable embellishments, have we fallen back into the paradoxes of realism? Not necessarily, for it is not now asserted that there is a *perfect* analogy between the model and the world, only that there is an analogy in certain respects (which we may call its *positive analogy*), and that this may extend further than has hitherto been investigated. There may seem to be little point in talking about 'models' at all unless there is some respect in which the analogy they exhibit breaks down. Atoms are thought of as being *like* billiard-balls, and not as *being* billiard-balls precisely because it is known that there are some respects (the *negative analogy*) in which they are *not* like billiard-balls. The whole strength of the formalist view of theories lies in its assertion that it is possible to abstract from the model the positive analogy which represents the extent of assured knowledge about the phenomena, and to throw away the negative analogy which might render the model misleading. We have seen that a theory cannot in general be tested or extended if reduced to a bare formalism, but what of a theory which (like Maxwell's) has been tested to breakdown and whose range of applicability and limits are hence known? Hertz declared that Maxwell's theory *is* the formal structure of Maxwell's equations, and it does indeed seem that when we know the exact extent of the analogy which Maxwell's aether-model bears to phenomena, what is true or useful in it can be expressed formally without any 'as if' clause to introduce irrelevancies. Clearly the formalists are right to this extent: the purpose of using models is to make them unnecessary by so familiarising ourselves with the new field of discovery that it can be described by means of its own language, without comparison with something more familiar. The metaphorical language derived from the model may then become *dead metaphor* ('attraction', 'tubes of force'), in other words, it acquires a technical meaning from the context of new discoveries and loses its original associations. Or its meaning may retain some of the original associations, only becoming modified gradually as the extent of negative analogy becomes clear, thus 'particle' in physics may come to mean not 'hard, coloured, spherical object which . . .', but 'singularity in the electromagnetic field which . . .', or 'wave-packet which . . .', the dots indicating that an indefinite number of things may be said about any of these entities, just as an indefinite number may be said about ordinary physical objects, and that at any given stage of physics we do not know even implicitly what all these things are.

In fact, no field of inquiry is ever closed in such a way that its formal description exhausts all that physics ever wants to say about it. Even when the formal structure of a limited area is known, physics always strives to find a more fundamental and more general theory to embrace it. Theories which are isolated and, as it were, confined within formal fences are no longer *scientifically* interesting, however useful the *applications* of their formal descriptions may be, and when a new fundamental theory is discovered the description of even such a theory is in principle changed, as billiard-ball mechanics is changed by relativity theory, although in practical applications no formal change may be required.

The question of whether models are intended as real descriptions is however a different one. Because all models ultimately prove to exhibit only a limited analogy with things, and because discoveries of hidden relationships between things can ultimately be expressed in formal terms, or in a modified and technical use of words first used in connection with the model, it does not follow that these relationships are not factual. It was long ago accepted as fact that the world is round, although for Aristotle this was a precarious theory suggested by the model of the sun and moon and justified by phenomenal arguments; it was accepted that the earth goes round the sun; that chemical compounds consist of elements; that magnetism is electricity in motion; that wireless waves pervade space; and so on and so on. The frontier of fact is continually shifting, and this is precisely the progressive character of science. But in many cases this progress shows that the various models in terms of which new facts came to be understood and accepted, were themselves literally *false*, because the new facts were not exactly like the old facts with which they were compared. And if they were in fact false, then they could, logically, have been true, and this is sufficient to place all such theory-models in the category of factual statements, and to enable us to make finer distinctions between those which were better or worse approximations to the truth.

It should, however, be noticed that not all models introduced into physics are intended to be true descriptions in this way. Four different types of non-realistic use may be distinguished. Firstly, *archaic models* which are deliberately used for practical purposes, although they are known to be false. The extent of their usefulness depends on the extent of their positive analogy, and the extent to which their negative analogy can be neglected in particular circumstances. Thus a model of heat flow may be used in contexts where it is a sufficient approximation to the kinetic theory, and Newtonian mechanics may be used where the accuracy of relativity mechanics is not required. Secondly, *analogue machines* (of a steel-and-copper or a paper-and-pencil kind) may be deliberately constructed to simulate certain aspects of natural processes, usually in order to act as computers where the mathematical theory of the phenomena is either not known, or is known but intractable. Examples of this use of models are the electronic tortoises, where there is an obvious negative analogy in certain biological and chemical respects between the model and the animal, but a positive analogy of unknown amount in some aspects of behaviour; or wind tunnels, where the fundamental mathematical theory is known, but is intractable in complicated special cases. These models are used in place of mathematical deductive theories whose details are not yet known, and they are not themselves intended as true descriptions, but only as aids to the discovery of such descriptions. Thirdly, *post hoc models* may be invented to embody an existing mathematical theory largely or solely in order to make the mathematical theory easier to apply, or to demonstrate its consistency. Examples would be the nineteenth-century mechanical aether-models, whose positive analogy was wholly contained in the corresponding equations, and which did not therefore contribute directly to the extension or testability of the theory, and were not intended realistically. Fourthly, there are *complementary models* such as the wave and particle models in quantum physics, which exclude each other in certain respects and which therefore limit each other's positive analogy, but whose potential positive analogy is unexhausted in other respects so that each can still function as a useful model in particular circumstances.

. . . No doubt other kinds of model could be distinguished in the practice of physics and the other sciences, but this brief classification serves to suggest a definition of the reality-status of a model. *A model is intended as a factual description if it exhibits a positive analogy and no negative analogy in all respects hitherto tested, and if it has surplus content which is in principle capable of test,* where 'in principle capable of test' is to be understood in a wide sense which will be explored in relation to some historical examples. Models which satisfy this criterion may be called *descriptive models.* It may seem that continued use of the word 'model' in relation to this definition is paradoxical, since what is here envisaged is potentially a literal, not a metaphorical, description, and that a model which satisfied these criteria would not require an 'as if' clause. But in view of the potential but as yet unexplored positive analogy, retention of the 'as if' is a useful reminder that the model may turn out to be a *false* description, and in any case use of 'model' may be understood to underline its *intelligible,* not its metaphorical, character. It is a model in the sense of a blueprint which copies phenomena as accurately as possible, not in the sense of an impression or caricature which deliberately distorts. The property of theories of embodying models so that they are rendered meaningful, and can be tested and extended, may be called their *intelligibility,* and this will be a necessary condition for theories in addition to the confirmation and falsifiability criteria already mentoned. Intelligibility is clearly also related to the intuitive idea of explanation according to which we wish not only to correlate phenomena and to be able to make predictions, but also to *understand* their connections, and this desire in large part accounts for the long persistence of models drawn from familiar mechanisms.

A particularly important class of descriptive models or theories in the science of any given period are those which may be called *fundamental,* in that they are more general than others and presupposed by them. A model will be fundamental only in relation to a particular historical situation, for example Democritan atoms, Newtonian attractive and repulsive particles, classical electrodynamics, and quantum electrodynamics, are fundamental relative to their historical context. These models do not fall naturally into the hypothetico-deductive hierarchy in terms of which theories are generally described, because in these terms they seem to be functioning at once as low-level generalisations, as high-level hypotheses, and as rules of inference. Take, for example, Newton's laws of motion in classical physics. In one sense these are low-level generalisations from the experimental facts about moving bodies. In another sense they are high-level hypotheses from which, in conjunction with other observations and generalisations, prediction and explanation are given of diverse physical phenomena. And in yet another sense, they are rules in accordance with which deductions from hypotheses are carried out. Such fundamental models have had little attention in current writing in the philosophy of science, but . . . the mode of action of bodies upon each other is one of the general properties which such models exhibit, and indeed the sense of 'action at a distance' or 'contact action' cannot be determined except in terms of the fundamental model and the concepts which it implies. . . .

STEPHEN TOULMIN

Ideals of Natural Order

*Born in London in 1922, Stephen Toulmin was a Fellow of King's College,
Cambridge, where he studied mathematics and physics. He did graduate
work in philosophy under Ludwig Wittgenstein. He was a University
Lecturer at Oxford for five years, and was Professor of Philosophy and
head of the philosophy department at Leeds University for five years.
He has also taught as a visitor at Melbourne University in Australia and
at Columbia and Stanford Universities in the United States. He is now
Director of London's Nuffield Foundation for the History of Ideas. Besides* Foresight and Understanding, *he is the author of* The Place of
Reason in Ethics, Philosophy of Science, *and, with his wife, June Good-
field, of* The Fabric of the Heavens *and* The Architecture of Matter.
*He has also written numerous articles in the philosophy and history of
science.*

What is a phenomenon? How do scientists tell when an event has
to be recognized as a 'phenomenon'; and how do they know what
sort of a phenomenon it is? The predictivist view of explanation
distracts our attention from this question, and that is a pity. For it
suggests that, when it comes to applying our theories, all events are
on a par—in the same way that all tides, sunrises, and eclipses are
to the forecaster. If we have a technique for predicting high-tides
or eclipses at all, it must apply equally to all such events; and why
(one might begin by asking) should it be any different with
explanation?

There is, in fact, an important difference here. A prognosticator
may forecast all events of a given type equally, but for the scientist
a phenomenon is not just *any* event of the sort he is interested in—
it is (as the lexicographers rightly say) 'an event . . . whose cause
is in question', and particularly one which is 'highly unexpected'.
Further, if a phenomenon is an unexpected event, this indicates, not
that the scientist neglected or simply failed to predict it, but rather
that he had certain prior expectations, which *made* the event unexpected.

From Stephen Toulmin, *Foresight and Understanding* (Bloomington: Indiana
Univ. Press, 1961), pp. 44–61. Used by permission of Indiana University Press,
and of Hutchinson & Co (Publishers) Ltd, London.

So far as the prognosticator is concerned, the course of Nature need consist only of 'one damn thing after another'. He himself is not going to be caught napping, for he has discovered a way of telling what is going to happen next; but this is not to say that he understands what is happening. The scientist is in a very different position. He *begins* with the conviction that things are not just happening (not even just-happening-regularly) but rather that some fixed set of laws or patterns or mechanisms accounts for Nature's following the course it does, and that his understanding of these should guide his expectations. Furthermore, he has the beginnings of an idea what these laws and mechanisms are, so he does not (and should not) approach Nature devoid of all prejudices and prior beliefs. Rather, he is looking for evidence which will show him how to trim and shape his ideas further, so that they will more adequately fit the Nature with which he wrestles.

This is what makes 'phenomena' important for him. The games-player improves his sporting techniques most quickly by playing against opponents who are just *one* degree his superior. The scientist, likewise, is on the look-out for events which are not yet *quite* intelligible, but which could probably be mastered as a result of some intellectual step which he has power to take. So long as everything proceeds according to his prior expectations, he has no opportunity to improve on his theories. He must look out for deviations that are not yet explained, but promise to be explicable.

'Deviations'—as soon as one begins to characterize phenomena, the very ink in one's pen becomes saturated with revealing words like 'deviation', 'anomaly', and 'irregularity'. All these imply quite clearly that we know of a straight, smooth, regular course of events which would be intelligible and rational and natural in a way that the 'phenomenon' is not. And this is just the conclusion we are now prepared for: the scientist's prior expectations are governed by certain rational ideas or conceptions of the regular order of Nature. Things which happen according to these ideas he finds unmysterious; the cause or explanation of an event comes in question (i.e. it becomes a phenomenon) through seemingly deviating from this regular way; its classification among the different sorts of phenomenon (e.g. 'anomalous refraction') is decided by contrasting it with the regular, intelligible case; and, before the scientist can be satisfied, he must find some way of applying or extending or modifying his prior ideas about Nature so as to bring the deviant event into the fold. Let us now look at some representative cases in which this intellectual procedure is displayed, so as to show something of the function which 'ideals of natural order' have in the development and application of scientific theory.

We may at this stage look back once again into the history of science, this time turning our attention to the seventeenth century. That period saw drastic changes in several branches of science, including two quite fundamental reorientations, which will be our chief topics in this chapter and the next. To begin with, let me illustrate the points I have been making by reference to the internal re-ordering within the science of dynamics, through which Newton's basic conceptions finally displaced those of Aristotle. In the next chapter we shall look at some changes which began seriously only at the end of the seventeenth century, and affected, not the internal organization of one science, but rather the mutual relations between two different sciences—physiology and matter-theory.

In each case a purely chronological account can be given of the experiments and publications and empirical discoveries of the scientists involved; but the intellectual changes which took place in their thought are intelligible only if we go deeper, and attempt to recognize the fundamental patterns of expectation at stake in the disputes. Happenings of sorts which earlier men had accepted as the natural course of events now came (we shall see) to be regarded as complex and anomalous; while others, which had earlier appeared exceptional, anomalous, or even inconceivable, came to be treated as perfect instances of the natural order. But let us get down to the cases.

First, consider the seventeenth-century revolution in dynamics. To bring out clearly the central change this involved, we must begin by looking at the popular caricature of pre-Galilean theories of motion, which can ultimately be traced back to Aristotle. 'Men's ideas about dynamics before Galileo,' this caricature suggests, 'rest upon a simple mistake. Aristotle was a philosopher, or at best a naturalist, rather than a true scientist: he may have been skilled at collecting specimens and miscellaneous information, but he was bad at explaining things; and he put forward certain clearly mistaken views about the ways in which the motion of a body is related to the forces acting on it. The benighted man asserted that the effect of a given force acting continuously upon a given body was to keep it in motion at a constant speed; whereas we have now looked and seen that a constant force produces not a constant speed but a constant acceleration. Aristotle's successors, having an exaggerated idea of his intellectual capacities, trusted to his words rather than to their own eyes, and only the work of that obstinately common-sensical genius Galileo—who refused to allow himself to be befuddled by mere words, and insisted on submitting even the most august and authoritative doctrines to the test of experience—led to this chimaera being blown away into the oblivion where it properly belonged.'

So stated, this may be less a caricature than the caricature of a caricature; though in less blatant forms, or in part, or by implication, one comes across this view often enough. Still, the picture implicit in this account, both of Aristotelian mechanics and of Galileo's own contribution to our thought, embodies a collection of anachronisms and legends exceptional even for the history of science —a subject in which the George Washingtons have for too long been chopping down their fathers' cherry trees. What one must protest against is not only the intrinsic unlikelihood that a man of Aristotle's capacities could have fallen for so elementary a blunder; but even more, the way in which this caricature degrades a fascinating episode into a prosaic one.

What, then, is wrong? To begin with, this picture gives Aristotle credit for attempting to do something he never seems to have envisaged. It treats him as putting forward a mathematical relationship of the sort familiar from modern dynamical theory. The relationship in question could be written either in words, as

Force varies as Weight times Speed

or alternatively in symbolic shorthand, as

$$F \propto W \times V$$

But this can be read into Aristotle's works only through an anachronism. We scarcely encounter this sort of mathematical equation before the sixteenth century A.D.—not just because the notation employed had yet to be developed, but because the very ideas implicit in the use of such equations were worked out only in the years immediately preceding 1600.

Of course, if we accept this equation as an expression of Aristotle's view, and interpret it in modern terms, we shall find it sadly mistaken. For nowadays it would be natural to take the symbol for speed as meaning 'instantaneous velocity', and the symbol for force in its standard Newtonian sense—both of them notions formulated with complete clarity only in 1687. At once objections arise. The term 'weight' now appears entirely out of place, and should presumably be replaced by the term 'mass'; and even so, the ratio of the force acting on a body to its mass surely determines not its velocity but its acceleration. Yet the question ought to be asked: are we taking Aristotle in a sense which he ever intended? If we read things into him, it will not be surprising if we end up by finding him seriously at fault.

How else, then, can Aristotle's thesis be taken? In general, his practice in the *Physics* is to put forward, not precise equations, but at most ratios or proportionalities relating (say) the lengths of time different bodies will take to go the same distances when different degrees of effort are exerted upon them. He presents these examples as concerned with *tasks:* posing his questions in the form: 'If such-and-such a task takes such-and-such a time, how long will such-and-such another task take?'—e.g. if one man can shift a given body 100 yards by himself in one hour, how large a body can two men jointly shift through the same distance in the same time? Aristotle concludes that, within limits, the amount a body can be displaced by a given effort will vary in inverse proportion to the size of the body to be moved; and also, that a given body can be displaced in a set time through a distance directly proportional to the effort available.

Of course (he allows) beyond certain limits this sort of ratio does not apply: a body may be so large that it can be shifted only by a team of men, and will not respond at all to one man working single-handed—he cites the instance of a team of men moving a ship. And he further remarks, with equal truth, that the effect one can achieve by a given effort depends entirely on the resistances to be overcome. A team of men pulling a ship will take longer to go from one point to another across rough ground than to move it the same distance over smoother ground. As a first approximation, and lacking any better definition of 'resistance', Aristotle accordingly puts forward the further proportionality: that the distance travelled in a given time will vary inversely as the strength of the resistance offered to motion.

Three things need saying about these ratios of Aristotle's, before we look at the dynamical innovations of the seventeenth century. The first is this: Aristotle concentrated his attention on the motion of bodies against appreciable resistance, and on the length of time required for a complete change of position from one place to another. For a variety of reasons, he never really tackled the problem of defining 'velocity' in the case when one considers progressively shorter and shorter periods of time—i.e. instantaneous velocity. Nor was he prepared to pay serious attention to the question how bodies would move if all resisting agencies were effectively or completely removed. As things turned out, his hesitations were unfortunate; yet his reasons for hesitating are understandable, and in their way laudable. Though he was a philosopher—and so, in some people's eyes, bound to have had his head in the clouds and his feet off the ground—Aristotle was always unwilling to be drawn into discussing impossible or extreme examples. Leaving aside free fall for the moment as a special case, all the motions we observe going on close around us happen as they do (he saw) through a more-or-less complete balance between two sets of forces: those tending to maintain the motion and those tending to resist it. In real life, too, a body always takes a definite time to go a definite distance. So the question of instantaneous velocity would have struck him as over-abstract; and he felt the same way about the idea of a completely unresisted motion, which he dismissed as unreal. In point of fact (I suppose) he was right. Even in the interstellar void, where the obstacles to the motion of a body are for practical purposes entirely negligible, there do nevertheless remain some minute, if intermittent, resistances.

In the second place: if we pay attention directly to the kinds of motion Aristotle himself thought typical, we shall find that his rough proportionalities retain a respected place even in twentieth-century physics. Interpreted not as rival laws of nature to Newton's, but as generalizations about familiar experience, many of the things he said are entirely true. One can even represent him as having spoken more wisely than he knew. For, where he argued only for rough, qualitative ratios connecting gross measures of distances and time, contemporary physics actually recognizes an exact mathematical equation corresponding closely to them—though, of course, one which relates instantaneous variables of a kind Aristotle himself never employed.

This equation is known as 'Stokes' Law'. It relates the speed at which a body will move when placed in a resisting medium, such as a liquid, to the force acting on it and the thickness (viscosity) of the medium. According to Stokes, the body's speed under those circumstances will be directly proportional to the force moving it, and inversely proportional to the liquid's viscosity. Suppose we take a billiard ball and drop it through liquids of different viscosities in turn—water and honey and mercury: in each case it will accelerate for a moment, and then move steadily down at a limiting (terminal) speed determined by the viscosity of the liquid in question. If the impressed force is doubled, the speed of fall will be doubled: if one liquid is twice as viscous as another, the billiard ball will travel at only half the speed.

The third point combines these two previous ones. The fact is that Aristotle based his analysis on one particular explanatory conception or *paradigm*, which he formulated by considering examples of a standard type; and he used these examples as objects of comparison when trying to understand and explain *any* kind of motion. If you want to understand the motion of a body (in his view) you should think of it as you would think of a horse-and-cart: i.e. you should look for two factors—the external agency (the horse) keeping the body (the cart) in motion, and the resistances (the roughness of the road and the friction of the cart) tending to bring the motion to a stop. Explaining the phenomenon means recognizing that the body is moving at the rate appropriate to an object of its weight, when subjected to just that particular balance of force and resistance. Steady motion under a balance of actions and resistances is the natural thing to expect. Anything which can be shown to exemplify this balance will thereby be explained.

In the case of bodies moving against a sufficiently slight resistance, as we all know, Aristotle's analysis ceases to apply. If you drop a billiard ball through air instead of through water or treacle, it will go on accelerating for a long time: under normal terrestrial conditions, it could never fall far enough to reach the 'terminal velocity' at which Stokes' Law would begin to apply. The factor of paramount importance in this case will for once be the initial period of acceleration, and that was something to which Aristotle paid very little attention. If he had thought more about the problem of acceleration, indeed, he might have seen the need for something more sophisticated than his simple proportionalities.

As things turned out, Strato, the very first of Aristotle's followers to take an active interest in mechanics, turned his attention at once to this very phenomenon. Yet, for many reasons—some of them intellectual, some of them historical—neither he nor his ancient successors made any great progress beyond Aristotle's ratios. It was left to the Oxford mathematicians of the early fourteenth century to add an adequate definition of acceleration to Aristotle's previous accounts of speed, and so to pave the way for the work of Stevin and Galileo and Newton.

So much for the background: what, then, did happen in dynamics during the seventeenth century? Certainly the popular caricature is wrong in one respect: men did not suddenly become aware that Aristotle's views about motion were false, whereas their predecessors had trusted blindly in their truth. Aristotle himself stated his ratios as applying only within certain limits, and John Philoponos (around A.D. 500) made it absolutely clear that projectiles and freely falling bodies could be explained only by bringing in some radically new conception. The problem was, *how* to remedy matters.

In retrospect we can see that the paradigm at the heart of Aristotle's analysis had to be abandoned and replaced by another, which placed proper importance on acceleration. Yet this was not easy: men were accustomed to think of motion as a balance between force and resistance, as much on the basis of everyday experience as through 'blind trust in Aristotle's authority'. They took the necessary steps hesitantly, a bit at a time, and in the face of their inherited common-sense. The most radical single step was taken by Galileo, yet even he stopped short of the conclusion which is generally credited to him.

There is nothing uniquely natural or rational, Galileo rightly insisted, in a terrestrial body coming to rest when outside forces are removed: rest and uniform motion alike, he argues, are 'natural' for a body on the Earth. Let us only approach gradually towards the extreme case of zero resistance, which Aristotle had denounced as impossible, and we shall recognize this. Think of a ship (say) on a calm sea, and imagine the resistances to motion progressively reduced, until we could neglect them entirely. If that were to happen, said Galileo, the ship would retain its original motion without change. If it had originally been at rest, it would remain at rest until some outside force started it moving; while, if it were originally moving, it would go on travelling along the same course at the same speed until it met an obstacle. Continuous, steady motion could therefore be just as natural and self-explanatory as rest, and outside resistances alone could bring terrestrial bodies to a halt.

By this step, Galileo went a long way towards the classical New-tonian view, but he did not go the whole way. True, he had ex-changed Aristotle's paradigm of natural motion—the horse-and-cart being pulled along against resistances at a constant speed—for a very different one. For Aristotle, all continuous terrestrial motion was a 'phenomenon', or departure from the regular order of things, and he would have asked: 'What is to keep Galileo's imaginary ship moving?' Galileo, however, now demanded only that we account for *changes* in the motion of bodies. His ship could move for ever with-out a motive force.

Now this result looks, at first sight, very like our modern 'law of inertia'. Yet Galileo's paradigm was no more identical with our own than Aristotle's had been. For what he envisaged as his ideal case was a ship moving unflaggingly across the ocean along a Great Cir-cle track, for lack of any external force to speed it up or slow it down. He saw that uniform motion could be quite as natural as rest; but this 'uniform motion' took place along a closed horizontal track circling the centre of the Earth; and Galileo took such circular mo-tion as entirely natural and self-explanatory. He does not seem to have regarded the ship as constrained by its own weight from flying off the Earth on a tangent—the image which can clearly be found in Newton.

Indeed, if Galileo's imagined ship *had* taken off from the sea and disappeared off into space along a Euclidean straight line, he would have been no less surprised—in fact, *more* surprised—than us. We should have one possible hypothesis at hand to explain this amazing event—namely, that the action of gravity on the ship had been sus-pended, so that it was no longer constrained to remain in contact with the Earth's surface and could fly off along its natural path. For Galileo, however, this option was not yet available: in his eyes, some active force alone could have obliged the ship to travel in a perfectly rectilinear path, instead of cruising of its own accord round its nat-ural Great Circle track.

When we turn to Newton we find that the ideal of natural motion has changed yet again. The fundamental example is completely idealized. From now on, a body's motion is treated as self-explana-tory only when it is free from all forces, even including its own weight. Galileo could explain his conception of 'inertia' by referring to real objects—ships moving on the sea. Newton started his theory by offering us a completely abstract example as the paradigm—namely, a body moving at uniform speed in a Euclidean straight line—and this, as Aristotle would have retorted, is the last thing we should ever encounter in the real world. But, then, Newton does not have to claim that, as a matter of fact, any actual body moves exactly as his first law specifies. He is providing us, rather, with a criterion for telling in what respects a body's motion calls for explanation; and what impressed forces we must bring to light if we are to succeed in explaining it. Only if a body ever were left completely to itself would it move steadily along a straight line, and no real body ever actually is placed in this extreme position. This is, for Newton, simply a dynamical ideal, the sole kind of motion which would be self-explanatory, free of all complexity, calling for no further comment—if it ever happened.

It should be clear, by now, why I present Newton's first law of motion or principle of inertia as an 'ideal of natural order'—one of those standards of rationality and intelligibility which (as I see it) lie at the heart of scientific theory. At their deepest point, the seventeenth-century changes in dynamics, which had been brewing ever since the early 1300's, involved the replacement of Aristotle's common-sensical paradigm by Newton's new, idealized one. From some angles, this could look like a regression: from now on it was necessary, for theoretical purposes, to relate familiar everyday happenings to idealized, imaginary states-of-affairs that never in practice occur—ideals to which even the motions of the planets can only approximate. Yet the change paid dividends. Once this new theoretical ideal was accepted, the single hypothesis of universal gravitation brought into an intelligible pattern a dozen classes of happenings, many of which had previously been entirely unexplained; and, in the resulting theory, Newton could display a whole new range of relationships and necessities as part of the intelligible order of Nature.

This example has illustrated how the idea of explanation is tied up with our prior patterns of expectation, which in turn reflect our ideas about the order of Nature. To sum up: any dynamical theory involves some explicit or implicit reference to a standard case or 'paradigm'. This paradigm specifies the manner in which, in the natural course of events, bodies may be expected to move. By comparing the motion of any actual body with this standard example, we can discover what, if anything, needs to be regarded as a 'phenomenon'. If the motion under examination turns out to be a phenomenon—i.e. 'an event . . . whose cause is in question' as being 'highly unexpected'—the theory must indicate how we are to set about accounting for it. (In Newton's theory, this is the prime task of the second law of motion.) By bringing to light causes of the appropriate kind, e.g. Newtonian 'forces', we may reconcile the phenomenon to the theory; and if this can be done we shall have achieved our 'explanation'. Every step of the procedure—from the initial identification of 'phenomena' requiring explanation to the final decision that our explanation is satisfactory—is governed and directed by the fundamental conceptions of the theory.

No wonder that the replacement of one ideal of natural motion by another represents so profound a change in dynamics. Men who accept different ideals and paradigms have really no common theoretical terms in which to discuss their problems fruitfully. They will not even *have* the same problem: events which are 'phenomena' in one man's eyes will be passed over by the other as 'perfectly natural'. These ideals have something 'absolute' about them, like the 'basic presuppositions' of science about which R. G. Collingwood wrote.

If that is so, the problem at once arises: how do we know which presuppositions to adopt? Certainly, explanatory paradigms and ideals of natural order are not 'true' or 'false', in any naive sense. Rather, they 'take us further (or less far)', and are theoretically more or less 'fruitful'. At a first, everyday level of analysis, Aristotle's paradigm of uniform, resisted motion had genuine merits. But a complete mathematical theory of dynamics required a different ideal. It was no good first taking uniform, resisted motion as one's paradigm, and supposing that one could later explain how bodies would move in the absence of resistances by cancelling out the counteracting forces: that way inevitably led to the unhelpful conclusion that a completely unresisted motion was inconceivable— since the attempt to describe it in everyday terms entangles one in contradictions. (Suppose you reduce the resistances finally to zero, then, in Aristotle's ratio of motive force to resistance, the denominator becomes zero; and you are landed in all the difficulties which spring from 'dividing by nought'.) On the contrary: it was necessary to proceed in the opposite direction. One must first start by taking entirely unresisted motion as one's ideal of perfectly simple and natural motion; and only later introduce resistances—showing how, as they are progressively allowed for, the uniform acceleration produced by a single force gives way to the uniform terminal speed of a horse-and-cart.

Changes in our ideals of natural order may sometimes be justifiable, but they do have to be justified positively. In due course uniform rectilinear motion became as natural and self-explanatory to Newton's successors as rest had been for Aristotle. Yet neither view of inertia was self-evidently correct: each must be known by its fruits. So its tenure as the fundamental ideal of dynamics was conditional, and provisional. For just as long as we continue to operate with the fundamental notions of the Newtonian theory, his principle of inertia keeps its place in physics. Yet, at the most refined level of analysis, it has already lost its authority. As one consequence of the twentieth-century changeover to relativity physics, the conception of 'natural motion' expressed in Newton's first law has again had to be reconsidered. The implications of the resulting amendments in our ideas may have been less drastic than those which flowed from the seventeenth-century revolution; yet—at the theoretical level—the change has been none the less profound.

Before we go on to our second example, let us return to a less rarefied atmosphere. The general point I am making does not apply only to abstract and highly developed sciences, such as dynamics. We use similar patterns of thought in the common affairs of daily life; and, in a sense, the task of science is to extend, improve on, and refine the patterns of expectation we display every day. There is a continual interplay between the two fields.

Suppose, for example, that we look out of the window, into the street. One car travels steadily down the road, comes into sight, passes our window, and goes on out of sight again: it may well escape our attention. Another car comes down the road haltingly, perhaps jerking and backfiring, perhaps only stopping dead and starting up again several times: our attention is immediately arrested, and we begin to ask questions—'Why is it behaving like that?' From this example it is only a step to the case of a practical astronomer, for whom the continued motion round its orbit of the planet Jupiter is no mystery: but for whom questions would immediately arise if the planet were suddenly to fly off along a tangent to its orbit and out into space: 'What made it do that?' And from this it is only one further step to the mathematicians' point of view, according to which, if left to itself, Jupiter ought to travel, not in a closed orbit, but in a straight line—so that even its normal, elliptical path demands explanation.

All the same: though the form of this thought-pattern is preserved, its content changes drastically, and one popular epigram about explanation is falsified in the process. For it is often said that 'explanation' consists in relating things with which we are unfamiliar (and which so need explaining) to others which are familiar to us (and so stand in no need of explanation). At a certain level this epigram has a point. If you are explaining something *to somebody*—what might be called an explanation *ad hominem*—it is sensible to start from things he knows about and understands, and to relate the things he finds mysterious back to those which he finds intelligible. This is one of the purposes of 'models' in the physical sciences. The beginner in electricity is helped to understand the relations between voltage, current, and resistance by having the flow of electricity in a wire compared with the flow of water down a tube: 'Don't you see? Voltage is like the head of water in the system, resistance is like the narrowness of a pipe, and the current of water or electricity depends in each case on both factors.'

Scientific discoveries, however, do not consist in arguments which are plausible *ad hominem*, but rather in explanations which will stand on their own feet. In these explanations, the relation between the 'familiar' and the 'unfamiliar' may be reversed. Revert for a moment to Newtonian dynamics: the ideal of inertial motion which underlies Newtonian explanations can hardly be described as *familiar*. (Aristotle would laugh at that suggestion.) If we were to insist on accounting for the 'unfamiliar' in terms of the 'familiar', instead of *vice versa*, we should never be able to shake ourselves loose of Aristotelian dynamics. Aristotle's paradigm is familiar in a way that Newton's never can be; and the Newtonian programme of treating the motion of horses and carts as being something highly complex, which can be understood only by starting from planets and projectiles and then allowing for a multiplicity of interfering forces —remains rather paradoxical to the commonsense mind.

What are the lessons of this first example? In ordinary life explanation may, perhaps, consist in 'relating the unfamiliar to the familiar'. But, as science develops, this turns into 'relating the anomalous to the accepted', and so in due course into 'relating the phenomena to our paradigms'. This is inevitable. Which things are familiar and which unfamiliar is a relative matter. (A man who lived in a desert might find the idea of 'the head of water' a difficult one to grasp, and be more mystified by hydraulics than by electricity.) On the other hand, whether an event is 'anomalous' or not need not be so personal a question. It can be discussed rationally—still more, if we go to the length of labelling the event as a 'phenomenon' and implying that it needs to be squared with theory. For then our standard must be, not what is familiar, but rather what is intelligible and reasonable in the course of Nature. And where we are led once we recognize this distinction, it has been the aim of this chapter to show.

Bibliography

In addition to Pap's *An Introduction to the Philosophy of Science*, the following work is an excellent general survey of the field:

Nagel, E. *The Structure of Science*. New York: Harcourt, Brace, 1961.

Besides the works from which the selections in this anthology are taken, the following are recommended:

Braithwaite, R. B. *Scientific Explanation*. Cambridge: Cambridge Univ. Press, 1953.

Hanson, N. R. *Patterns of Discovery*. Cambridge: Cambridge Univ. Press, 1958.

Kemeny, J. G. *A Philosopher Looks at Science*. Princeton: Van Nostrand, 1959.

Mehlberg, H. *The Reach of Science*. Toronto: Univ. of Toronto Press, 1958.

Popper, K. R. *The Logic of Scientific Discovery*. New York: Basic Books, 1959.

Scheffler, I. *The Anatomy of Inquiry*. New York: Knopf, 1963.

Schlesinger, G. *Method in the Physical Sciences*. London: Routledge, 1963.

Toulmin, S. *The Philosophy of Science*. London: Hutchinson's Univ. Library, 1953.

Some other useful anthologies are:

Danto, A., and S. Morgenbesser. *Philosophy of Science*. New York: Meridian Books, 1960.

Feigl, H., and M. Brodbeck. *Readings in the Philosophy of Science*. New York: Appleton, 1953.

Feigl, H., *et al. Minnesota Studies in the Philosophy of Science*. Minneapolis: Univ. of Minnesota Press, I (1956); II (1958); III (1962).

Madden, E. H. *The Structure of Scientific Thought*. Boston: Houghton, 1960.

Wiener, P. P. *Readings in Philosophy of Science*. New York: Scribner, 1953.

The leading journals in the field are:

British Journal for the Philosophy of Science. Thomas Nelson & Sons, Ltd, Parkside Works, Edinburgh 9, Scotland.

Philosophy of Science. Department of Philosophy, Michigan State Univ., East Lansing, Michigan.